THE HOROLOVAR 400-DAY CLOCK REPAIR GUIDE

BY
CHARLES TERWILLIGER

OVER 35,000 COPIES SOLD

First Edition	July 1953	2,122
Second Edition	July 1954	2,108
Second Printing	May 1955	3,078
Third Edition	September 1956	5,180
Fourth Edition	January 1959	5,100
Second Printing	February 1963	3,219
Fifth Edition	September 1965	3,012
Second Printing	June 1967	3,200
Third Printing	August 1969	3,326
Sixth Edition	March 1972	5,000

Author: CHARLES TERWILLIGER
Escapement Section: HENRY B. FRIED
Editor: GENE WAGGAMAN
Layout: JACK FORCE, JR., ROBERT MAITLAND
Plate Drawings: ETHEL SCHELZ, VEE GUTHRIE, ROBERT MAITLAND
Photography: PETER IRELAND
Typography: MORRIS & WALSH
I. B. M. Typewriter: WEAVER ORGANIZATION
Mechanicals: ROBERT MAITLAND, JOHN HARRINGTON, BOB ROBINSON
Lithography: GENERAL OFFSET COMPANY, INC.
Cover Stock: HOLLISTON MILLS' ROXITE
Publisher: THE HOROLOVAR COMPANY

Library of Congress
Catalogue Card Number 65-24619

Printed in U.S.A.

3

FOREWORD

Since 1949 the German 400-Day Clock has become a particular favorite in American homes. Not only have the clocks been extensively imported from Germany, but thousands of them have been received here as gifts from retail stores and Post Exchanges in all parts of the world. This vigorous activity, together with the increased demand for the clock, has had the additional effect of bringing many "old timers" out of hiding. Today, there may well be close to five million 400-Day Clocks in this country, with more coming in every day.

As a result, repairmen are being asked to service increasing numbers of clocks, although many of them would literally prefer not to have the business. Their reluctance usually stems from an inability to estimate accurately the time necessary to clean, repair and, particularly, to *regulate* the clock properly. However, these functions can be performed easily, and without costly loss of time. Let's look first at the most common problems:

The part most frequently in need of attention and replacement – the pendulum suspension spring – presents the greatest single problem. If the exact strength of the suspension spring required for the clock is unknown, the repairman wastes time, effort and expense, since he is forced to the trial and error procedure of attaching and detaching springs of different strengths.

The second problem seems to center on the escapement which is considered the source of trouble in the performance of the clock much more often than it should be. And, there are a number of other factors about the 400-Day Clock which differ sufficiently enough from other clocks, and particularly from watches, to lead many repairmen to create problems where none actually exist.

Curiously enough, neither clock nor suspension spring manufacturers have given much thought to the repairman's problem. For instance, even if the correct strength spring for each manufacturer were known, the repairman would still be handicapped by the fact that most clocks are not identified by their manufacturer's name. Actually, many are marked only with the name of the *importer*, who, all too often, is mistaken for the manufacturer. And to make identification even more difficult, there is the fact that not only are there a great *number* of importers, but also that the names of many of them will be found on clocks made by several manufacturers.

Suspension springs, themselves, have presented equally confusing problems, because of the variety of materials used in making them, and because of their different dimensions. Most of the older manufacturers made their springs of steel. Somewhat recently, bronze was used. Bronze, although more sensitive to temperature change than steel, will not rust. But, until Horolovar made Temperature Compensating Suspension Springs available in 1951, there had never been a spring which had the uniform standards of width and thickness necessary to answer the pendulum spring requirements of *all* 400-Day Clock manufacturers. Nor had there been springs which, in addition to having this quality of uniformity, would also compensate for temperature change, and would neither rust nor break. (See Page **160**)

The purpose of this Repair Guide, then, is (1) to assist the repairman in determining quickly and simply the proper strength Horolovar Temperature Compensating Suspension Spring to use in repairing almost any 400-Day Clock, (2) to show, when possible, the correct position in which the blocks and fork should be attached to the suspension spring, (3) to explain in detail the operation and adjustment of the 400-Day Clock escapement, and (4) to answer the many questions which repairmen have so often asked about repair of the clock.

We wish to acknowledge the many repairmen who have taken the time to furnish details about clocks which were not represented in previous editions. We also wish to acknowledge the assistance received from Mr. J. E. Coleman, editor of "Clockwise and Otherwise" in *The American Horologist and Jeweler*.

Charles Terwilliger
July 1, 1965

SECTION 1 . . . ADJUSTMENT AND REPAIR OF THE 400-DAY CLOCK ESCAPEMENT

More questions about repair of the escapement are asked than about any other part of the 400-Day Clock. We sincerely hope that this important chapter of the Guide will explain everything you'll need to know, and that it will save you hours of time in making your repairs.

We have obtained the help of Henry B. Fried in the writing of this article. Few men can bring to you the knowledge which he has amassed from his vast experience with the technical aspects of horology. Certified Master Watchmaker, instructor, lecturer, author of *Watch Repairer's Manual** and *Bench Practices for the Watch Repairer*†, Mr. Fried is a past president of the Horological Society of New York and the New York State Watchmaker's Association, and vice-president of the Horological Institute of America. He is also Technical Director of the Watch Material Dealers Association and an honorary member of many other horological organizations. In 1955, he received the Outstanding Achievement Award of the U. H. A. of A. As Instructor of Horology for the Board of Education, New York City, and Horological Editor of *Jeweler's Circular-Keystone* (magazine), he is in constant daily contact as consultant with the horological problems of both student and professional.

This article has been especially written in language which can be understood by the layman. The precise illustrations accompanying the text, drawn by Mr. Fried, are designed not only to show the correct relationship between pallets and escape wheel teeth, but also to show what actually happens when both correct and incorrect adjustments are made.

Charles Terwilliger

Introduction

This section is devoted to a detailed study of the type of 400-Day Clock escapement having a 20-tooth escape wheel (Figure 1) and anchor with adjustable pallets (Figure 2).

Figure 1

Escape wheels with 15 teeth (Figure 3) are frequently used in these clocks, particularly in miniature movements, but the same basic principles outlined for the 20-tooth wheel apply equally well to them.

*D Van Nostrand Company, New York, N.Y. - $5.95

†Roberts Publishing Company, Denver, Colorado - $4.95

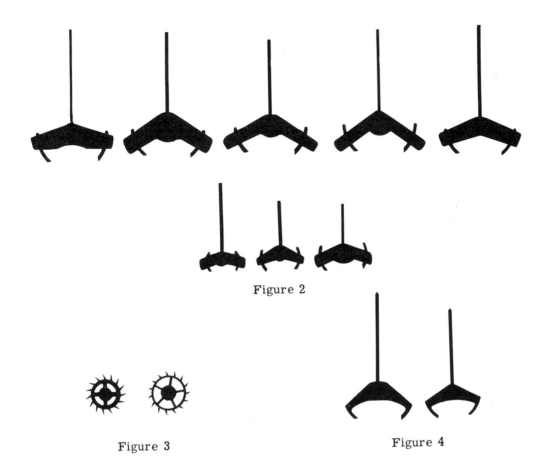

Figure 2

Figure 3   Figure 4

Anchors with "solid" pallets (Figure 4) are also frequently used with both 20-tooth and 15-tooth escape wheels. However, since these pallets are not adjustable, the problems concerned with them are less complicated than those arising with the adjustable type provided, of course, that the pallets have been made properly.

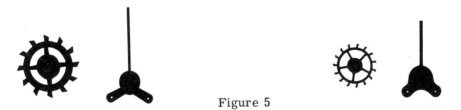

Figure 5

Another type of 400-Day Clock escapement, known as "pin pallet," (Figure 5) is to be found occasionally. The "pin pallet" anchor differs from anchors with adjustable or solid pallets in that it has a pair of steel pins set perpendicularly to the anchor frame. In this type of escapement, the slanted impulse surface (later described) is on the escape wheel tooth and is actuated by the anchor pallet pin. With the adjustable pallet and solid pallet type of anchor, the slanted impulse surface is on the pallet, and it is actuated by the escape wheel tooth. (There are usually only 12 or 15 teeth on the escape wheel). The same basic principles outlined for the adjustable pallet escapement apply equally well to the pin pallet escapement.

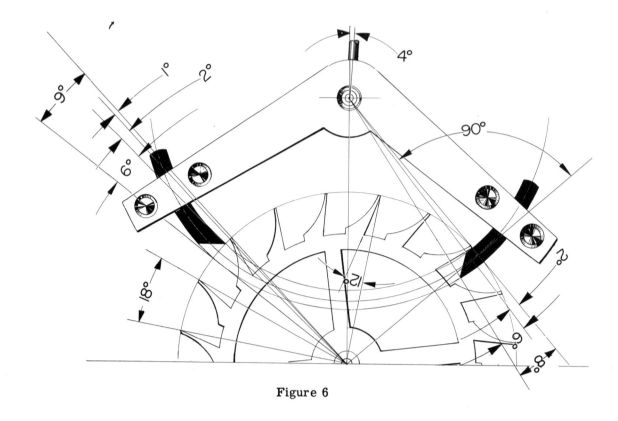

Figure 6

Explanation of the Escapement Action

Figure 6 shows the adjustable pallet escapement viewed from the back plate where the repairman can best observe the escapement action through the especially made "peep holes" (See Figure 10) which appear in most movements. Ten of the escape wheel's twenty pointed teeth are shown here. The two hard-polished steel pallets, attached to the anchor, are shown in black. Each pallet is held by a clamp screwed to the anchor frame (on the back of the frame in the illustration shown) or by just the head of a screw.

The pallet on the left is called the "receiving" or "entrance" pallet, because, in the escapement action, the escape teeth enter into the anchor following contact with it. The pallet on the right is called the "exit" or "discharging" pallet, because the teeth leave the anchor following contact with it.

This type of escapement is called *dead-beat*, because the escape teeth remain motionless while locked on the pallets' curved surface despite any movement of the pallets. In other types of anchor escapements, there is a recoil, or backward movement, of the escape wheel during such action.

A careful study of Figure 6, with the following observations, will aid in an understanding of the escapement action:

This particular escape wheel travels in a clockwise direction. (In clocks where the escape wheels turn in a counter-clockwise direction, teeth and pallets are in reverse positions). The 20 teeth are spaced 18° apart. The front of each tooth has a rake (slant) of 12° back from a radial line. This front slant of the tooth is necessary so that only its tip

8

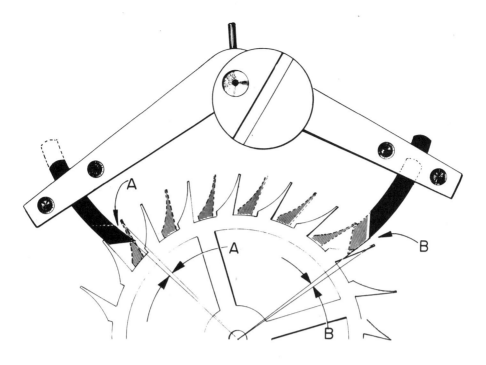

Figure 7

makes contact with the curved surface of the pallet during what is known as the *locking sequence* of the escapement action. If the tooth were not slanted, the corners of the pallet, especially the exit pallet, would scrape the front surface of the tooth, causing a recoil of the wheel which would stop the action.

In Figure 6, an escape wheel tooth has just dropped off the receiving pallet while the fifth tooth in front of it has become locked on the exit pallet. The distance between the dropped tooth and the sharp *let-off* edge of the entrance pallet is 2° while the tooth thickness at its tip is 1°. The width or thickness of each pallet is 6°. Thus the combined widths of the tooth thickness, pallet and drop space equals 9° or the equivalent of half a tooth space. The 2° drop space represents the amount of free, unhampered movement of the escape wheel between contact with either pallet. Each pallet (see exit pallet) allows for an angular swing of 8°. Of this, 2° is on the circular locking surface and 6° is for the actual lifting action which takes place as the tooth slides over the slanted or impulse surface. Therefore, the 8° angular motion of the pallet causes the anchor pin at the top of the anchor to swing an initial 4° each side of the line-of-centers. Motion of the pin beyond this is caused by the momentum, or overswing, of the pendulum.

In fine regulator clocks, the teeth are more pointed, and they lock closer to the impulse surface of the pallets. The lifting action is seldom more than 2°. These refinements are impracticable in the 400-Day Clock. First, the tooth tips must be made stronger to withstand bending if they should fail to drop off the pallet, and, because of some mis-action or disturbance, be forced back on the locking surface. Second, the lock has to be deep enough to prevent the escape wheel from unlocking prematurely should any undue vibration be given to the oscillating pendulum.

A drop space of 2° is necessary for the safe functioning of the escapement. Notice that both pallets swing along the same circular track. When one pallet is being lifted to un-

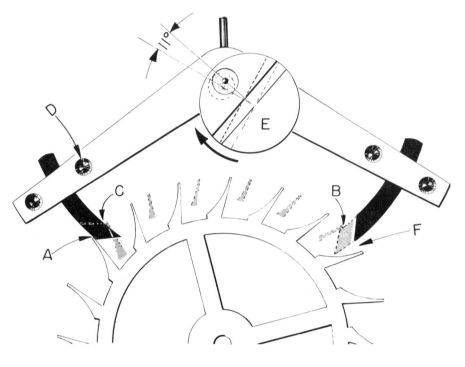

Figure 8

lock the escape tooth, the opposite pallet with its sharp edge is descending into the escape wheel. If the space is less than 2°, this sharp edge will dig into the back curve of the tooth, thereby preventing any further movement of the pallets or of the escape wheel.

The impulse action must be relatively large, compared with the drop action, to provide a sufficient twisting of the suspension spring to maintain the pendulum motion.

Examining and Testing the Escapement

First, remove the pendulum and the entire suspension unit. (With some clocks, it will also be helpful to remove the suspension bracket.) Next, place your finger on the tip of the anchor pin, and move it back and forth slowly, checking all 20 escape teeth for correct locking and also observing whether they escape, or drop freely, from the entrance pallet. Repeat this observation on the exit pallet. Next, observe whether the drop space for all 20 teeth is the same off the entrance pallet as off the exit pallet. Figure 7 shows this test in application. When a tooth is locked on the entrance pallet, there are five teeth between the pallets. In this position, the drop space is at B and is called "outside drop," because the dropping of an escape tooth took place *outside* the anchor as did the locking. In the shaded view, which shows the alternate position, there are 6 teeth inside the anchor, a tooth locked on the exit pallet and a tooth dropped from the entrance pallet. This is called "inside drop," shown at A, because both the lock and drop took place *inside* the anchor.

In a well adjusted escapement, the inside drop space A and outside drop space B must be equal *for all teeth.* If the drop spaces are unequal for any of the 20 teeth, it is an indication that some of these teeth may be bent. A smaller amount of inside drop space on

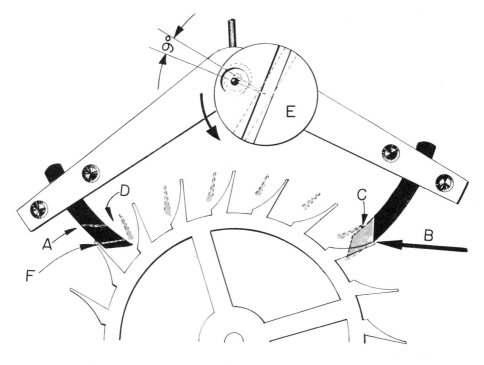

Figure 9

one tooth may indicate that a tooth locked on the exit pallet is bent forward or the tooth just dropped (See A, Figure 11) is bent backward. If the outside drop space is smaller on one tooth, it may show that the dropped tooth is bent backward, or the tooth locked on the entrance pallet is bent forward.

If the escapement action is being examined for the purpose of determining some fault in the clock, and it is found to be perfectly adjusted as described here, you may be certain that the fault lies elsewhere. Don't make adjustments to the escapement unless you are sure they are absolutely necessary.

Making Adjustments to the Escapement

Many repairmen, watchmakers in particular, who are unfamiliar with the 400-Day Clock escapement, make the mistake of comparing the escapement action with that of a watch. They notice that the escape wheel teeth lock quite deeply on the 400-Day Clock pallets and they reason that, since this condition is detrimental to a watch's action, they should try to make the lock shallower by giving a clockwise adjustment of the eccentric nut E*, Figure 8. Such an adjustment does carry the anchor upward, thereby lessening the locking, but the new position of the anchor causes multiple errors. (This short locking is shown at A and in the shaded alternate view B, Figure 8.) First, the safe lockings necessary for this type of escapement are disturbed. Second, the slot in the eccentric nut, twisted with a sharp screwdriver has probably been gouged making subsequent corrections difficult. (See Question 2, page 20) But the greatest upsetting of the adjustment occurs at F and at C, Figure 8. By turning the eccentric nut clockwise an angular distance of 11°, or a linear distance of only about 1/32 of an inch (approximately 1 millimeter) the outside drop space F is greatly increased at the expense of the inside drop space C shown in the

---

*Some clocks have a different method of adjusting the position of the anchor pivot hole. In fact, in at least one miniature movement, the eccentric nut carries the escape wheel pivot rather than the anchor pivot.

11

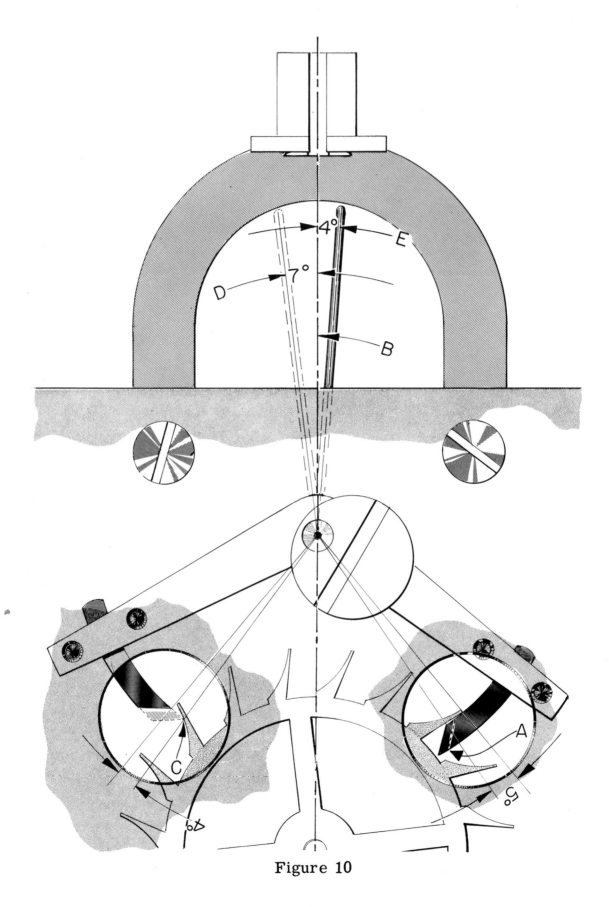

Figure 10

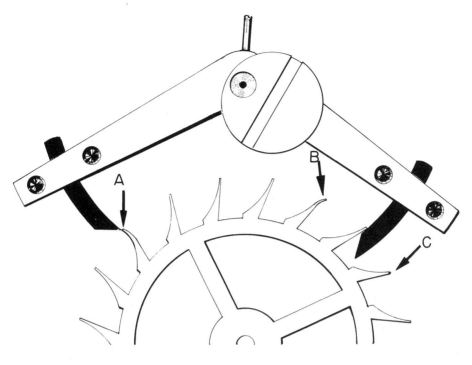

Figure 11

alternate view.

With this maladjustment, the escapement is out of action and the clock will not run. The escape tooth shown at B will not unlock because, when the opposite pallet descends during the unlocking attempt, it will dig into the back of the shaded tooth at C.

If the eccentric nut had been turned counterclockwise, the opposite effect would have been achieved. The locks are deepened. F, Figure 9, shows the original position of the pallet before the eccentric nut E was turned. The distance below the dotted line at F indicates the increase in lock. C shows how the exit pallet lock is increased. A shows the position of this pallet when the exit pallet is in the locking position. Turning the eccentric nut only 9° causes the outside drop space B to disappear, while the inside drop space D is greatly increased. The escapement in this condition is inoperative.

About Adjusting the Pallets

Suppose the eccentric nut is left untouched, but one of the pallets is moved. What is the effect? Figure 10 illustrates what will take place. Here the exit pallet has been moved downward the distance from its original position shown by the dotted line A. This increased the lock from 2° to 5°.

Because the pallet, to unlock, must now go up 3° further than it did previously, the opposite pallet will be required to descend a corresponding additional 3°. You should always remember that an increase of the lock on one pallet increases the lock on the opposite pallet a similar amount. (Increasing the lock on both pallets doubles the effect on *each*

13

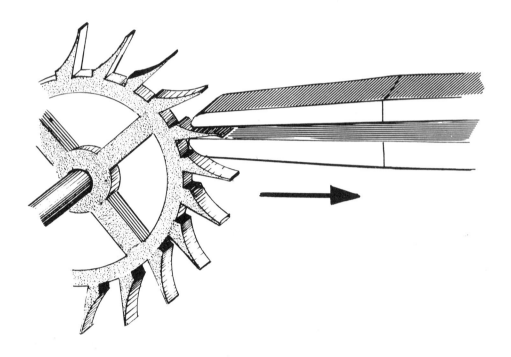

Figure 12

pallet.)

Increasing the lock to 5°, as illustrated in Figure 10, will make the escapement inoperative. Since the exit pallet must now rise 5° before the escape tooth will become unlocked, the opposite pallet, when it has gone down but 4°, will butt the curved back of the tooth shown at C, stopping the escapement and leaving a tooth hung up at 1° on the exit pallet's locking surface.

Furthermove, the anchor pin will move more from the line of centers on one side than on the other. This is shown in the upper section of Figure 10. Here the anchor pin at D travels 7° to the left of the center line B while the anchor pin at E still remains at the original 4°. (If it is possible that the escapement is still operative, a resetting of the suspension unit will be necessary to put the clock in beat again.)

In Figure 10, the "peep holes" found in most back plates are indicated with shading. It's through these holes that all observations of the teeth and pallets must be made. Some of the pre-World War I clocks did not have these holes and, on these clocks, the adjustments must be viewed from the sides, which is much less convenient.

Summary of Adjustments

Up to this point, we have covered the general adjustments to the escapement. The following is a review in chart form of the basic adjustments that can be made. When the adjustments indicated in this table seem to have a combination of symptoms, treat each symptom separately.

TROUBLE SHOOTING CHART

COMMON SYMPTOMS				CORRECTIONS			
Entrance Pallet Drop	Exit Pallet Drop	Entrance Pallet Lock	Exit Pallet Lock	Eccentric Nut *	Entrance Pallet	Exit Pallet	Pallet Lifting Surface Angles†
More	Less	Normal	Normal	Raise Pivot Hole			
Less	More	Normal	Normal	Lower Pivot Hole			
Normal	Normal	Deep	Deep		Move Up	Move Up	
Normal	Normal	Shallow	Shallow		Move Down	Move Down	
More	Less	Deep	Deep	Raise (§) Pivot Hole			
Normal	Normal	Deep	Shallow		Move Down		Make Entrance Pallet Steeper
Normal	Normal	Shallow	Deep			Move Down	Make Exit Pallet Steeper
Normal	Normal	Very Shallow	Deep			Move Down	Make Exit Pallet Steeper
Normal	Normal	Deep	Very Deep			Move Up	Make Exit Pallet Less Steep

* It is assumed that the eccentric nut carries the *anchor* pivot. If it carries the *escape wheel* pivot, correction should be made just the opposite to that indicated.

† Rather than attempting to grind and polish the pallets, you may find it more convenient to replace them.

§ If the locks become shallow in making this adjustment, consider this a new symptom and make further corrections as indicated.

Note these three basic rules of thumb:

(1) If drops are equal, do not move the eccentric nut.
(2) If drops are unequal, do not move the pallets.
(3) If locks are unequal, change the lifting surface angle of one or both pallets.

TABLE OF ADJUSTMENTS

WHEN YOU DO THIS:			THE RESULT IS THIS:			
Eccentric Nut	Entrance Pallet	Exit Pallet	Entrance Pallet Lock	Exit Pallet Lock	Entrance Pallet Drop	Exit Pallet Drop
Raise Pivot Hole			Decreases	Decreases	Decreases	Increases
Lower Pivot Hole			Increases	Increases	Increases	Decreases
	Move Up		Decreases	Decreases	No Change	No Change
	Move Down		Increases	Increases	No Change	No Change
		Move Up	Decreases	Decreases	No Change	No Change
		Move Down	Increases	Increases	No Change	No Change
	Move Up	Move Up	Decreases*	Decreases*	No Change	No Change
	Move Down	Move Down	Increases*	Increases*	No Change	No Change

by the total of the combined distances both pallets are moved.

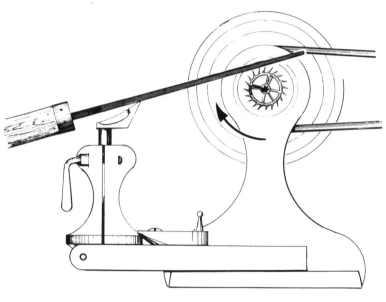

Figure 13

Repairing the Escapement

Repairs differ from adjustments. "Adjustment" means altering the position of one or more parts in relation to others. "Repairs" are considered to be a changing of the physical appearance of the part itself, in order to make it function properly.

Repairing Damaged Teeth

Sometimes the escapement will seem to be in good order, but at irregular intervals the escape wheel will trip off the pallet, instead of locking on it as it should. The clock may even run for a while in this condition, but its timekeeping would be most erratic. Or, sometimes a tooth will be hung up and fail to drop off the pallet, stopping the escapement, even though to casual inspection the teeth may seem to be in good shape.

Both of these conditions are most often caused by short, bent or broken escape wheel teeth. If you realize that it takes about five minutes for the escape wheel to make a single revolution, you can see why one such tooth can avoid immediate detection unless you make a thorough test of every tooth on each pallet.

Figure 11 shows an escape wheel with a tooth bent backward at A, one bent forward at B, and a broken tooth tip (short tooth) at C. In this Figure, although the tooth which is locked on the exit pallet is perfectly formed, the tooth which is bent backward at A has caused the escapement to stop operating, because the inside drop space no longer exists and the escape wheel cannot unlock.

When tooth B locks on the exit pallet, the same fault will be observed, because the forward bent tooth keeps the inside drop space (off the receiving pallet) below minimum requirements needed for clearance.

If a short tooth (one with a broken tooth tip) drops off the receiving pallet, it will cause a light lock on the tooth which is about to drop onto the exit pallet. This tooth will also lock

16

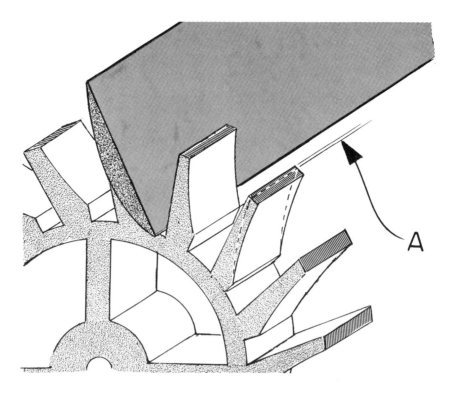

Figure 14

too lightly on either pallet.

To test for deformed teeth, hold your finger on the tip of the anchor pin and move it very slowly, observing the escapement action through the peep-holes in the back plate. Permit each escape tooth to move slowly across one pallet's lifting surface. When a tooth drops off the pallet, arrest the action of the anchor pin so that no further movement is permitted. Now inspect the lock on the opposite pallet and make a mental note of the amount of this lock. Repeat this on all 20 teeth for drop and lock. Any deformed or broken tooth can easily be located by observing obvious differences in the amount of a tooth's drop or lock.

Repairing the Pallets

Since the pallets are extremely hard tempered and move about 25 times slower than those on swinging pendulum clocks of the same size, they should wear much longer. Also, since the escape teeth are much broader than those of swinging pendulum clocks they distribute their wear over a broader area of the pallets' polished surfaces. Since they receive such little wear, the pallets should never need repair. Nor should their shape be changed in any way. It is best to leave the pallets alone. They should be raised or lowered only if it's absolutely necessary.

If a shift of one or both pallets is indicated, you can most easily make it by using the Horolovar Adjustable Pallet Setter, illustrated and described on page 167.

Repairing an Escape Wheel

When an escape tooth is bent, you can often straighten it by grasping the bent tooth between the blades of a pivot-straightening tweezer and pull-snapping it while squeezing the

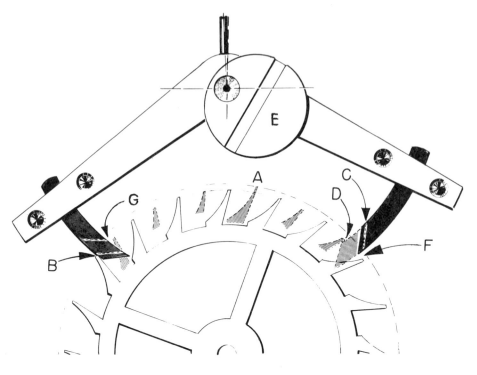

Figure 15

tweezers. This method is shown in Figure 12. Too much pressure on the tweezers is not recommended, for this might thin out the end of the soft tooth and raise a burr.

If you find an escape wheel with a short or broken tooth, it's best to obtain a new wheel, or a complete new wheel and pinion. If the wheel is from an old clock and you cannot match it, you can substitute one with the same number of teeth and approximately the same diameter. Sometimes it's possible to obtain a complete wheel and pinion which can be made to fit.

If you can get a complete unit, check these four things, in addition to the wheel's diameter: (1) The escape wheel must be in the same horizontal plane as the anchor, and aligned so that the wheel teeth strike the middle portion of the pallets. If they don't, it may be possible to shift the position of the anchor or the wheel on the arbor so that both will be in the same plane. (2) The diameter of the pinion should be as close to that of the original as possible. (3) The pinion should be positioned so that it makes full contact with the center wheel. (4) The pivots should be of the same diameters as those of the originals. If they are too large, either they should be reduced to fit; or, you should carefully broach the pivot holes. If they are too small, you can bush or carefully close the holes.

If a substitute wheel is not available, you can make a new one, or have one made, to the original sample. In cases where only the tip of the tooth is missing, you can shorten all of the other teeth on the escape wheel to the height of the shortest tooth. This operation, called "topping," is performed as follows: Place the escape wheel in the lathe as shown in Figure 13 and run the lathe, moderately fast, in the direction of the arrow. Steady a fine file on the adjusted T-rest, and bring it to bear gently on the wheel. This action cuts the teeth shorter without bending them, and without raising burrs on their front surfaces where the finest surface is needed for smooth operation.

Make frequent inspections during this operation to insure that the teeth are not cut too

18

short. If they are cut too short, the 12° rake (slant) will be insufficient to provide clearance for the locking corner of the exit pallet. The pallet will then dig into the front side of the tooth, causing the escape wheel to recoil and possibly causing the clock to stop.

When the teeth are shortened, their tips naturally become thicker, thereby reducing the available drop space. If they are found to be excessively thick, you can thin them by a judicious filing of the back curve of each tooth, as shown in **Figure 14**, until the tooth-tips become as thin as the space shown by the arrow A. A curved file or an India oilstone slip can be used. This operation will also remove any burrs, if any remain from the topping shown in **Figure 13**.

When the wheel is finished in this manner, fit it to the movement. A trial manipulation of the anchor will reveal that the escape teeth, formerly high as that at A, **Figure 15**, now only reach to the pallets at dotted line B and C. In this condition, the escape wheel will cause the anchor to trip back and forth like an alarm clock bell hammer. Therefore, both pallets will have to be extended to the amount indicated in black, *below* the dotted lines B and C. Extending both pallets equally will most likely provide the safe lock shown at B, and the alternate position D.

Here it should be pointed out that, in theory, the operation described above is not sound, since it upsets the geometric proportions of the original escapement design. In actual practice, however, the method has provided to be a workable repair expedient.

Do not expect to achieve the same result by lowering eccentric nut E. It will not work for the following reasons: The smaller the escape wheel, the closer its arbor must be to the anchor arbor and the smaller a circle must be scribed by the curved pallets. As mentioned above, if the escape wheel is made smaller than the original by topping, the geometric proportions in which the escapement was designed originally no longer exist. Turning down the eccentric nut will bring the escape wheel and anchor arbors closer, but since the circle scribed by the curved pallets cannot be made of a smaller diameter, because their shape is fixed, the disproportion remains uncorrected. Furthermore, turning the eccentric nut down causes the outside drop to disappear, as shown in Figure 9.

When the escape wheel was made smaller, the drop space was also slightly decreased. However, if the teeth are made thinner, the drop spaces will be sufficient as shown at G at inside drop, and the alternate position F at outside drop, in Figure 15.

SECTION 2 ... ANSWERS TO THE MOST FREQUENTLY ASKED QUESTIONS ABOUT 400-DAY CLOCK REPAIR

The following thirty-five questions and answers appear to cover most of the problems which will confront you. However, if you are faced with a specific repair problem not covered somewhere in this Guide, or if you have other questions about the clock, we'll gladly try to help. Write: Question Department, The Horolovar Company, Box 400, Bronxville, New York 10708. If the question is about repair, give as many details of the symptoms, and the steps you have taken, as you possibly can. And ... *be sure to enclose a self-addressed, return envelope.*

QUESTION (1): How do you adjust a 400-Day Clock escapement?

ANSWER:
Questions about the 400-Day Clock escapement have been asked so frequently that there appeared to be great need for a thorough explanation of this major part of the clock as well as for details covering its adjustment and repair. Therefore, Section 1 of this Guide, written with the help of Henry B. Fried, one of the country's foremost authorities on watch and clock escapements, has been devoted entirely to this subject.

A thorough reading of Section 1 should give you full knowledge of the fundamental principles of the 400-Day Clock escapement and also answer any questions about its adjustment and repair.

QUESTION (2): How can you turn a tight eccentric nut without chewing up the sides of the slot?

ANSWER:
There seems to be no standard among manufacturers for either the size or tightness of the eccentric nut. Some nuts can easily be turned with a screwdriver; others offer so much resistance that it is almost impossible to move them without injuring the sides of the slot.

Actually, it is best not to use a regular screwdriver at all, not even to test the tightness. Since the slot sides are parallel, and a screwdriver's end is tapered, all pressure put on the screwdriver is directed only upon the top edge of the slot. It's bound to leave an ugly scar.

At almost any hardware store, you can buy a tool known as an offset screwdriver for less than fifty cents. It is all steel, has two useable ends and gives better leverage than a regular screwdriver. Grind one end so that it fits into the slot, making sure that the flat sides are parallel. With this tool, there is little likelihood of your damaging the sides of the slot while you're turning. The other end of the screwdriver may be ground to fit a different size slot.

If the eccentric nut has obviously never been turned before, it is more than likely that it doesn't need turning now. (Be sure to read Section 1 "Adjustment and Repair of the 400-Day Clock Escapement" before you start moving the nut.) If you find that it is necessary to move it, first make a tiny scratch across the edge of the nut so you will not only know how far you move it, but also what position it was in originally. You may wish to put it back exactly where it was!

In recent times, several manufacturers have replaced the eccentric nut with a U-shaped, die-stamped area around the anchor pivot hole, leaving the hole out on an arm. Here, adjustment is made merely by bending the arm slightly up or down. It makes adjustment simpler, but its chief disadvantage lies in the fact that, if it's moved too often, the arm and hole will break off.

QUESTION (3): How can you stop the anchor from fluttering?

ANSWER:
This question is often worded in other ways. For example: "I replaced a suspension spring with **HOROLOVAR** of the proper strength indicated, but the clock now gains an hour every hour. I used a thinner spring, but it still gains several hours in a day. Is there something wrong with the springs?"

What has happened is that, unnoticed, the anchor fluttered. That is, the escape wheel skipped several teeth during one turn of the pendulum. Actually, for the clock to gain an hour every hour, the pendulum would have to rotate back and forth at a speed of sixteen times a minute!

Fluttering usually takes place when a suspension spring has been replaced with the fork set too low. You can remedy this by raising the fork slightly on the suspension spring. Very seldom is it necessary to touch the escapement to cure this fault. However, many repairmen immediately go to work on the pallets in an attempt to make the correction and, in so doing, throw the escapement all out of proportion.

For the correct position of the fork on the suspension springs of clocks imported since 1949, see Section 5.

QUESTION (4): How much clearance should there be between the anchor pin and the fork tines?

ANSWER:
There should be *only* enough clearance to insure that the tines do not bind the pin at any point in its movement. If the fork is spread open too wide, much of the power of the pin's impulse will be lost. If it is too tight, all of the power will be lost.

You should check the amount of clearance when the anchor pin is at its extreme angle, for when the pin is at its farthest point from center — in either direction — the clearance between pin and fork tines is at the minimum.

Although most forks are designed to minimize this condition, by having tines with rounded or knife edges, it is a good idea to check the clearance of the fork on the anchor pin every time the suspension unit is attached — especially since it is very easy to bend the tines without noticing it. This happens most often when a new suspension spring is being inserted in the unit.

QUESTION (5): How should a broken anchor pin be replaced?

ANSWER:
In several of the newer movements, the anchor pin is bent, or offset, to bring its top nearer to the fork. However, when viewed from the back, it should still be centered above the pallets. Adjusting the beat by bending the anchor pin actually makes a very easy job difficult, and may easily break the pin.

Anchor pins on most newer clocks are made of soft steel, but many on old clocks were tempered. When these older types break off, repairs are more difficult to make. If a soft pin was already bent when you received the clock, and you wish to straighten it, you can avoid possible breakage by grasping it with pliers just above the anchor and making the bend above this point.

If the pin is broken off so that a piece remains inside the anchor, the expedient (and most expensive) thing to do is to replace the entire anchor unit. However, if the piece is not tempered, it is possible to drill it out. Taper the end of a new steel pin, approximately 1 millimeter or less in diameter, and drive it tightly into the hole.

If a stub of the broken pin remains, try to remove it by unscrewing it, for some pins are threaded into the anchor. But, whether they're threaded or not, the simplest way to re-place a pin after the stub has been removed is to drive a new pin in the hole so that it is friction tight. A more skillful job can be done by tapping the hole and threading the new pin to fit.

Some repairmen replace broken pins by soft-soldering them back on to the anchor. Al-though this method can be used to perform a functional repair, and might conceivably be resorted to if a broken tempered pin cannot be removed from the anchor, it should be gen-erally discouraged. The use of solder in any visible place on the clock, no matter how carefully it's applied, is poor horological workmanship. It usually takes only a minute or more to do the job right.

If a soldered joint is to be made, it's best to use a soldering iron, rather than an alcohol lamp or a torch. With a lamp, and particularly with a torch, it's all too easy to reach a temperature which will seriously affect the temper in the pallets.

QUESTION (6): How do you put the pendulum in beat?

ANSWER:
First, it helps to know exactly what is meant by the pendulum being "in beat." This can best be understood by the following instructions with a reference to Figure 16.

Once the clock is started, it continues to run because the power, originating with the wound mainspring, is converted mechanically into a series of little impulses which indi-vidually push the rotating pendulum back and forth. This oscillating pendulum action originates with the escape wheel teeth (ewt) which, through the anchor pallets (p), pass al-ternate impulses on to the suspension fork (f) via the anchor pin (ap). The fork, in turn, transfers the back and forth motion of the anchor pin to a twisting motion of the suspen-sion spring (sp). The twist ultimately passes down the length of the spring to the bottom suspension block (bb) where it ends as a little push of sufficient intensity to maintain the oscillation of the pendulum attached to it.

To keep this action continuous, the push must be given to the pendulum at an equal dis-tance from its dead position in either direction. Otherwise the clock will soon stop. The adjustment by which the push is made equal in both directions of rotation is known as put-ting the pendulum "in beat."

Adjustment of the pendulum beat is made by turning the entire suspension unit on its axis (a-x). This is accomplished in one of several different methods depending upon the de-sign of the clock. In all clocks, the suspension unit is held by its top block (tb) in some form of saddle (s). Except in one or two of the very early models, provision has been made for this saddle to be turned. It may be necessary to loosen a set screw (ss) to move it, or the saddle may just be friction tight (ft).

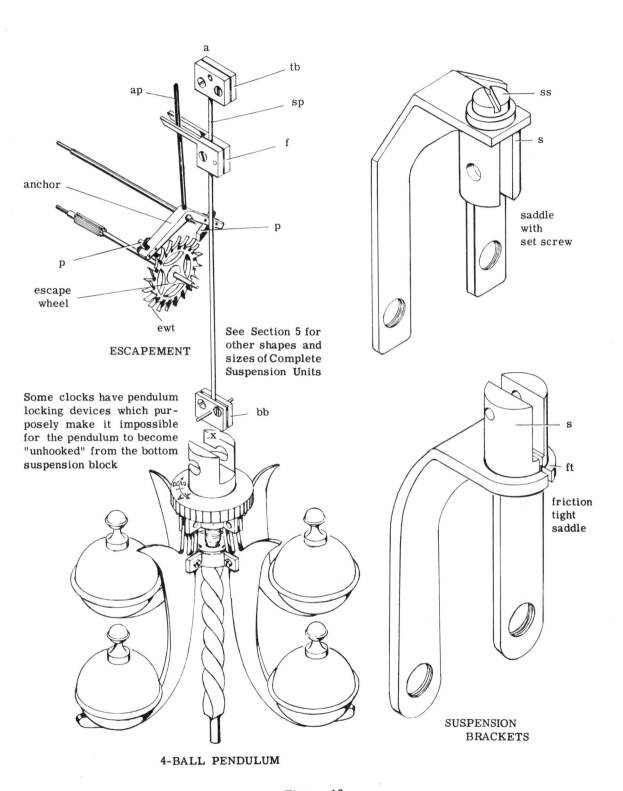

a

tb

ap

sp

f

anchor

p

p

escape
wheel

ewt

ESCAPEMENT

See Section 5 for
other shapes and
sizes of Complete
Suspension Units

ss

s

saddle
with
set screw

Some clocks have pendulum
locking devices which purposely make it impossible
for the pendulum to become
"unhooked" from the bottom
suspension block

bb

x

s

ft

friction
tight
saddle

4-BALL PENDULUM

**SUSPENSION
BRACKETS**

Figure 16

In some old clocks, when the saddle is fixed, the adjustment can only be made by giving the suspension spring (sp) a slight but permanent twist at a point near the top suspension block (tb), a rather delicate operation best accomplished with tweezers.

Here's how to find the correct position of the suspension unit which will put the pendulum in beat.

Check the clock to be sure that it's wound and that it's in a level position. Also, check the suspension spring (sp) to see that it is absolutely straight and that the two blocks (tb) and (bb) and fork (f) are in the same vertical plane as the spring. (If one of them is slightly out of line, it can be put back into position by twisting the spring a little. However, if the spring is badly bent or kinked it should be replaced.)

Start the pendulum rotating in either direction by giving it up to, but not more than one, full turn. Now focus your attention on the escape wheel teeth (ewt) as they are released, one by one, from the pallets (p). (If it is quiet, you will hear them tick.) Notice that the pendulum continues to swing a certain distance *beyond* the point at which the escape wheel teeth drop, or are released. This amount of pendulum overswing, i.e., the amount which the pendulum turns *immediately after* the escape wheel teeth are released, must be the same for both directions of swing. When this condition is satisfied, the pendulum is "in beat."

Any necessary correction can be made by turning the suspension unit as described in an earlier paragraph. Be sure to turn the unit in the direction in which the pendulum overswing is least. While only a very small adjustment is ordinarily necessary, it may well take several tries before the unit is correctly positioned. Beat setting is easier, faster and usually more accurate if performed with a beat setting tool (See page 164).

With clocks having saddles with set screws (ss), it is always a good idea to check the beat after the set screw has been tightened. The saddle may have been turned in tightening without your having noticed it.

QUESTION (7): How much should the pendulum rotate ?

ANSWER:
The minimum number of degrees that a pendulum of the standard size clock should turn, is about 270 or 3/4 of a turn. Anything less, particularly if there is little overswing, usually indicates a loss of power somewhere in the train.

It is sometimes possible to increase the turn of the pendulum by raising the fork slightly on the suspension spring. However, if this doesn't help, or if it impairs the functioning of the escapement, check the escapement action. If that is in order, then try to locate the source of the power loss. Look for too much play in the fork, a loose top block, a distorted mainspring, worn pivot holes, or gummy oil in pivot holes or mainspring barrel.

There's considerably more leeway in the *maximum* amount that a pendulum will turn. In the standard clock, a 360° to 450° turn (1 to 1 1/4 turns) is not unusual. As a matter of fact, some of the new miniature movements have pendulums that make up to two turns.

In general then, if the pendulum of a clock makes at least three quarters of a turn, and if there is an overswing of one half inch or more, you can be reasonably sure that the clock will run at least 400 days.

QUESTION (8): Is there any trick to regulating the pendulum so that the clock will keep good time?

ANSWER:
Actually no, — provided you take this precaution: When you reset the pendulum after each regulation, be sure not to turn it more than a very few degrees past its normal arc.

A great many 400-Day Clock owners, and even a great many repairmen, seem to feel that these clocks are just cheap novelties which shouldn't be expected to keep good time. This feeling has some basis in fact, since many clocks actually do not keep good time for a variety of reasons: (1) The clocks may be equipped with bronze or steel suspension springs. It is impossible for clocks equipped with suspension springs of these metals to keep good time. (See Horolovar Suspension Springs, page **160**) (2) The escapement may not be in perfect order. If the anchor has a jerky motion, for instance, the clock may run, but it will not keep good time. (3) The final regulation of the clock may not have been made carefully enough.

Many clock owners are not aware of the fact that their clocks are not completely regulated at the factory, or that they, themselves, must make the final regulation. All manufacturers include some sort of instructions on how to regulate the pendulum (some in better English than others!), but few stress the point that *several* adjustments must be made if good timekeeping is to be attained.

One word of caution: Before turning the regulating nut at all, it is well to determine which way to turn it to make the desired correction. For most ball pendulums, a clockwise turn of the nut will expand the position of the weights, thereby making the clock run slower. Sometimes arrow markings on the nut will also show you in which direction to turn. Turning toward A (Advance) or F (Fast) will speed the clock up; toward R (Retard) or S (Slow) will make it slow down. However, *don't blindly depend upon a clockwise turn of the nut to slow the clock down. Some of the new clocks do just the opposite!*

The best method to insure proper regulation is to keep a record of the day and hour when the clock is set, the amount of the change made and whether it was fast or slow. At first, you can make an adjustment every day or two, moving the pendulum regulating nut perhaps only a quarter of an inch at a time. Then, if the clock seems to show no great gain or loss of time, make your checking just once a week for two or three weeks. When the time comes that a shift of only 1/16th of an inch of the regulating nut (on a ball pendulum) determines whether the clock runs fast or slow, you know that you have it regulated as finely as possible.

The actual regulating operation should be performed on the pendulum regulating nut just as the pendulum is about to reverse its direction. If you wait for the pendulum to reach this point, you will be able to start it rotating again at this same point by merely releasing it from your fingers. If you swing the pendulum just a few degrees past its reversal point, no great harm will be done, but people who swing the pendulum so that it will rotate much more than its normal cycle after each regulation, immediately interject an error in the timekeeping of the clock which will correct itself only after the pendulum has returned to its normal cycle. In the meantime, the movement of the hands, having been slowed down somewhat by the long "overswing" of the pendulum, will indicate a loss of time. Although this would normally suggest that a *fast* regulation of the pendulum nut be made, such an adjustment might actually be unnecessary.

Some clock repairmen, with a knowledge of this phenomenon, reset the hands with their master timepiece only after the clock has run a few hours. This is, in fact, an excellent idea, but unfortunately, time consuming.

Often people ask why no one has made a chart which would relate the number of minutes a day that a clock could be made to gain or lose to a certain amount of turn of the pendulum regulating nut. As a matter of fact, such a chart would not be practical. The relationship would vary from model to model with differences in the type of pendulum, as well as in the diameters of the regulating nuts, being just two variables. A chart would have to be made for each clock.

QUESTION (9): *Do all 400-Day Clock pendulums make 8 turns per minute?*

ANSWER:
Until recently, practically all 400-Day Clock pendulums did make 8 turns per minute. Moreover, many repairmen used this fact as a reference point in regulating the clock, or in checking the correct strength of a new suspension spring. With a stop watch, or with the second hand of a watch or clock, they'd check the timing of the 8 turns. If it took less than, or more than, 60 seconds to complete the 8 turns, an adjustment would be indicated. But, at best, this method of regulating is only approximate.

In 1953, several clocks with miniature movements, and pendulums making 6, 8 and 10 turns per minute, appeared on the market. Since the number of pendulum turns per minute is usually not known for each clock and would have to be calculated, the old method of regulating is naturally no longer feasible. The best way of regulating these clocks, and, as a matter of fact, the older ones too, is to attach the dial and hands and follow the procedure as described in the answer to Question 11.

QUESTION (10): *How long should the suspension spring be?*

ANSWER:
The proper length of the suspension spring varies with the type of clock.

Most clocks imported since 1949 have a pendulum guide cup in the base, into which an extended axis of the pendulum is supposed to hang. The purpose of this cup is twofold: (1) It shows whether or not the clock is level, and (2) it prevents the pendulum from swinging freely when the clock is picked up, thereby guarding against a bent suspension spring or a broken dome.

The spring for clocks having these guide cups should be long enough to insure that the pendulum will remain suspended within the confines of the cup, but not so long that it will touch the bottom. Since the cup is seldom more than 3/16" deep, the spring should be measured carefully, especially if it is being cut from a longer piece.

The length of spring for clocks equipped with pendulum locking devices is even more critical. For some, a difference of 1/16" may make either the clock or the locking device inoperative. After installing a new suspension spring, check the locking of the pendulum, and the safe clearance between the pendulum and the locking bracket or socket, before putting the pendulum in beat and regulating.

Requirements are less precise for clocks having ball pendulums without guide cups or locking devices, or for those having old style disc pendulums. In these cases, the clock can be made to run properly even if the pendulum is as much as an inch or more above the base. However, the shorter a spring is, the thinner it will have to be if it is to be regulated properly.

Spring strengths indicated for the back plates in this Guide are correct for clocks with guide cups and pendulum locking devices, and for other pendulums which are approximately one quarter of an inch above the base. If a higher pendulum is desired, a somewhat thinner spring than the one indicated will have to be used.

QUESTION (11): What is the best way to determine whether a replaced suspension spring is of the correct strength for the clock?

ANSWER:
If the correct suspension strength for the clock is not known (or if the back plate of the clock is not illustrated in this Guide) the only thing to do is to select a spring of middle strength, such as an .004" (.102 mm) for a Standard size movement, or an .0025" (.064 mm) for a miniature movement, and try it out.

Some repairmen have made a practice of determining the correctness of the spring by timing the swing of the pendulum with the second hand of a watch or clock. If the pendulum made 8 turns in exactly one minute, they assumed, correctly, that the right spring was being used. However, with the appearance of the new miniature clocks, some of which have pendulums making 6, 8 and even 10 turns per minute, this method of timing has proved unreliable as well as time consuming.

A more practical method is to let the clock do its own checking while you go about your other work. If you are reconditioning the clock, leave the determination of the correct suspension spring strength until last. Replace the dial and hands, or just the hands if you have reason to want to keep your eye on the motion train. When you are ready to check the suspension spring, set the hands to the correct time, preferably using an electric clock with a sweep second hand as reference. Come back to it in five minutes, a half hour, or whenever it's convenient. Now, compare the position of the hands with those of the electric clock, and make an adjustment on the regulating nut of the pendulum if necessary. Reset the hands, and follow the same procedure until you're satisfied that you have the correct spring strength. (See Answer to Question 8: Is there any trick to regulating the pendulum so that the clock will keep good time?)

If you suspect that the suspension spring is not of a strength which will allow for regulation within the regulating limits of the pendulum, don't waste time making a series of small adjustments. Turn the regulating nut as far as it will go, and set the hands again to the correct time. The next check will tell you whether it's possible to turn the regulating nut back to a correct position, or whether the suspension spring will have to be changed.

On occasion, pendulums will be found that have been permanently altered one way or another and therefore require a spring strength that falls between two standard Horolovar strengths. In this case, use the stronger spring and thin it down a little by rubbing it up and down, between the bottom block and fork, with a folded piece of fine emery cloth. Do not remove the suspension unit from the clock, but keep the spring taut by pulling gently on the pendulum. Make only a few strokes at a time, to avoid thinning too much, and check the beat after each thinning to make sure that you have not given the spring a slight twist during the thinning operation.

QUESTION (12): How do you replace a suspension spring in a clock when the suspension blocks have no screws, but are just pressed together?

ANSWER:
The most satisfactory way to replace the suspension spring is to replace the existing cheaper top and bottom blocks for ones with screws. Competition among the German 400-Day Clock manufacturers became so keen for the U. S. dollar in 1952-1953 that several manufacturers reduced their cost without thought to possible future repair problems. Most of these manufacturers evidently saw the error of their ways, but in the meantime possibly 50,000 or more clocks with suspension springs of the type you have described found their way into U. S. homes. This is a sufficiently large number of clocks to make

27

it worth your while to glance at the suspension blocks of every clock before estimating on its repair. What may appear to be a simple suspension spring replacement may turn out to be a suspension *unit* replacement, with probably more than normal time needed to obtain the new unit or to repair the old one.

Usually the fork is attached to the spring in the customary way with a screw, so it can be reused.

It is possible to replace a suspension spring using the old blocks by prying them open, replacing the spring, and closing them again tightly with brass rivets. Here is the way it's done: Drill two small holes through the blocks, one on either side of the spring. Counter-sink them slightly, in order that the rivets will hold after their ends are filed flush. Be sure to remove any broken pieces of spring from the old blocks before inserting the new spring and, of course, make sure that the new spring is of the correct length and is correctly seated in the blocks before you rivet them.

The chief disadvantage of attempting to use the old blocks, by riveting them together, is that it's hard to know whether the spring is being held tightly enough. If the spring hasn't been held tightly and loosens when you test it, the riveting job has to be done all over again.

Although it is preferable to use the blocks made by the manufacturer of a clock, those of other manufacturers may be used. Just keep in mind that the top block must be able to move freely in the saddle, so that the suspension spring will always pull from the pivoting point, rather than from the bottom of the block, as it will if the fit is too tight. Also the bottom block must fit into the pendulum hook easily, so that the spring will not be bent when the pendulum is being attached or removed. To free a tight block, use a fine file to remove burrs from screw heads or ends, or increase the opening in the saddle or pendulum hook. Never attempt to open these by bending, for they will break very easily.

QUESTION (13): How tight should the hands be?

ANSWER:
The hands should turn very easily. If they're properly adjusted, you should be able to turn the minute hand with your little finger, without exerting much pressure.

The minute hand on some of the clocks imported in the 1950s was set so tightly that it is difficult to turn it without actually bending it. The pressure needed to turn it is so great that it forces the anchor to flutter no matter what position of the cycle the pendulum is in. (It is normal for the anchor to flutter, when the hands are being turned, while the pendulum is in the *middle* of its cycle. In fact, this is a test you can make to prove that the escapement is in order.)

Hands that turn stiffly are usually found in clocks that do not have a tension washer behind the cannon pinion. (See Question 14.) Tension is obtained from either a purposely crimped cannon pinion, or from a hand nut which presses tightly against the minute hand bushing, or from both.

A pinched cannon pinion is the result of poor design. It is to be found, along with other ill-advised economies, in clocks which have been assembled with price, rather than quality, in mind. There is nothing wrong with a design which allows hand tension to be obtained directly from the cannon pinion. Such an arrangement is found in many of the best clock movements. In these cases, the cannon pinion is fitted closely to the centerwheel arbor along a considerable length. Tension control is obtained from a split section of its tube, a distance of as much as a third of its length. With this design, it is possible to obtain a positive, yet easy movement of the hands.

The tube of the pinched 400-Day Clock cannon pinion is usually turned to a smaller diameter, for about 1/8th of an inch at its center, to make it thinner and thus easy to pinch. An examination of the cannon pinion will reveal that the actual pinching was done with a pliers-like tool which left only a small indentation where its two jaws bit into the brass. Since the entire tension control of the hands is limited to these two little indentations, it is easy to understand why this control is uneven, why it varies from clock to clock — too loose in some, too tight in others. Inevitably, the wear on just these two points is bound to cause trouble.

If tension is obtained just by pressure of the hand nut on the hand bushing, i.e., by squeezing the cannon pinion from end to end (without a tension washer), the clock will also inevitably give trouble.

The permanent cure for these conditions is to redesign the cannon pinion so that a tension washer can be put behind it. It means that the tube must be smoothed out on the inside and shortened in length by about 2 millimeters, by turning down the thickness of the pinion proper. There is usually enough room so that the thinner pinion will still engage the intermediate wheel without interference. However, you should always examine the relative thickness of the wheel and pinion, as well as the play in the intermediate wheel, to be sure that the operation can be performed successfully.

Unfortunately, it is not always possible to take the time required to make a permanent repair. The practical action to take, therefore, is to readjust the pinch in the cannon pinion so that the hands will turn with ease. This repair should be good for at least a few years.

The difference between hands which are too loose or too tight may be the difference of a few thousandths of a millimeter in the tightness of the hand nut on the end of the arbor. The nut is supposed to be tightened until it rests against a shoulder at the end of the threaded portion of the arbor. It frequently happens, however, that, even though it appears to be tight, the nut doesn't actually reach this point. The result is that, when the hands are turned backward, the nut backs off, and the hands get too loose. When the hands are turned forward, they get too tight. Not infrequently, when you try to manipulate this poor arrangement, either you strip the threads in the hand nut, or the threaded end of the arbor breaks off in the nut.

To correct the faulty condition of this design, it is often necessary to do some adroit filing, or to add some shims. If the hands are always too tight, or if you cannot make the nut stay tight, the minute hand bushing can be thinned down just enough to allow the nut to be drawn up tightly on the arbor while, at the same time, providing a smooth and easy turning of the hands. It might even be necessary to shorten the length of the cannon pinion, if the hand bushing is already thin. If the hands are too loose, a shim in the form of a bent washer can be inserted between the hand nut and the minute hand bushing, thereby providing a tension washer in front of the cannon pinion rather than behind it. Some manufacturers have, in fact, used this expedient. However, here again, the permanent repair should be to shorten the cannon pinion, as described above, so that a tension washer can be put behind it.

QUESTION (14): How important is the tension washer behind the cannon pinion?

ANSWER:
The purpose of the tension washer is to provide a sufficient amount of friction to the motion train, so that the drive from the center wheel arbor will be positive and yet will

allow for an easy manual "setting" of the hands. Not all clocks have a tension washer behind the cannon pinion, but clocks that do operate with one usually cause less trouble than those that do not.

Often when a clock is dismantled, this little washer is overlooked and lost. When the motion train is reassembled without it, the hands fall loosely, even when the hand nut (or pin) is tightened. In the repairman's attempt to make the hands tighter, the nut is often turned too hard. As a result, its threads are stripped or the threaded end of the center-wheel arbor breaks off.

Tension washers are of various designs — round, oval, triangular, etc. The shape is un-important, and it is not difficult to make a washer, if one is needed. Take a piece of steel from a broken mantle clock suspension spring, or from any similar thin, steel stock. Through it, drill a hole just large enough to fit loosely against the centerwheel arbor hub which is close to the front plate. Trim the thin steel around this hole so that you have a washer no larger in diameter than the portion of the cannon pinion which is not cut into by the pinion teeth. This procedure will assure that points of contact will not interfere with the ends of the intermediate wheel teeth. When this is done, curve the washer slightly, so that it will require a slight pressure from the cannon pinion to flatten it. This little pressure, or tension, is sufficient to assure a positive operation of the motion train and still allow the hands to turn freely and easily. (See also Question 13: How tight should the hands be?)

QUESTION (15):   *How is it possible for the hour hand to lose time even though it is tight on the hour wheel pipe? How can this fault be corrected?*

ANSWER:
Occasionally, incredible as it may seem, intermediate wheels and hour wheels from some clocks have been found to have one too many teeth ... an error which would have been discovered at the manufacturer's if the clock had been tested. This extra tooth will cause a lack of synchronization between the minute and hour hands. Although wheel cutting machines were corrected before many clocks having this fault got into production, the number of clocks which have reached the U. S. have been sufficient enough to cause many owners concern, and to baffle many repairmen.

There is only one way to make the correction. Locate the faulty wheel and replace it with one with the correct number of teeth.

QUESTION (16): *When you clean a clock, is it always necessary to remove the mainspring?*

ANSWER:
Definitely yes! Many repairmen are inclined to skip this important operation either be-cause they are too timid to remove the mainspring from the barrel, or because they realize that, even if they did remove it, they would be unable to replace it properly with-out a mainspring winder. To cover up this omission, they usually just add a little fresh oil to the old, and hope for the best.

If the clock is of very recent manufacture and its mainspring was inserted at the factory, you might get by, using this obviously slipshod method. However, it is unfair to the cus-tomer to neglect this important step. And, for three very good reasons, a neglected main-spring may be the source of considerable trouble for you:

(1)   The old oil may be so gummy that the mainspring coils actually stick to each other or to the barrel sides. This condition reduces power to such an extent

that the expedient of adding fresh oil will result in only a temporary improvement. Even though the clock may seem to run satisfactorily at the moment, it will probably be returned in only a few months. During this period, because its power will be erratic, the clock will not keep good time.

(2) One of the mainspring eyes may be torn. When the mainspring is wound, particularly if gummy oil is causing extra resistance, the eye may break. If it does, the resulting shock will usually cause major damage to the teeth of both barrel and first wheel. Should this happen while the clock is in your shop, you'll probably lose your profit on the repair.

(3) The coils of the mainspring may be distorted because some previous repairman replaced it in the barrel by hand, an almost impossible job to do without distorting the coils. If you have been making a regular practice of replacing the mainspring by hand, you'd better check your own work in this way: Remove the spring, after you've inserted it, and see whether the edges of the coils are parallel when you hold the spring by its end. The odds are better than ten to one that the coils will be distorted. When a distorted mainspring uncoils, much of its energy is lost in the pressure that the twisted coils exert on the sides of the barrel. This energy loss weakens the entire power train to a point where the clock will no longer run.

Since a 400-Day Clock mainspring winder (See page 166) is relatively expensive, and hardly worth the investment unless a specialty is being made of 400-Day Clock repairs, it is a fair question to ask how, then, can the mainspring be properly replaced? There are two answers: (1) Send the mainspring, barrel and arbor to someone who has a winder and will do the job for you, or (2) plan to replace the mainspring with a new one which will come to you already coiled to a diameter slightly smaller than the inside diameter of the barrel. (See page 163) Work the wire ring that's around the coil over to the edge of the coil, allowing the spring to be inserted *past* the top of the barrel hook. You can then pry off the ring, letting the coils spring open in the barrel. If the outer eye of the spring has not caught on to the barrel hook, do this: With the exposed part of the mainspring facing down, press the barrel firmly against the bench with the palm of your hand until the spring is in as far as it will go.

Insert the arbor, place the cover in position, and tap it around its edges with a fiber hammer until it falls into place. (You can use the padded jaws of a vise to give extra, but gentle, pressure against the lower half of the cover while you tap the upper half with a fiber hammer.) One complete turn of the arbor, with a key, is then usually enough to slip the spring around inside the barrel until the outer eye of the mainspring engages with the barrel hook. Remove the cover again and check to make sure that the inner coil and eye fit snugly around the arbor and arbor hook. It must not be possible for the arbor hook to free itself from the mainspring eye. Then oil (See Question 18), and replace the cover.

A word of caution about inserting a mainspring in a barrel, particularly if you don't own a winder. Check the direction in which the arbor hook is to fasten itself to the spring by placing the arbor in the barrel. Practically all 400-Day Clock mainsprings are coiled into the barrel counterclockwise. However, some of the pre-World War I clocks had barrels with mainsprings coiled clockwise.

QUESTION (17): *What is the purpose of the little extra barrel and mainspring attached to the third wheel in some clocks? How should it be set?*

ANSWER:
This unusual device appeared in some Standard size clocks manufactured by Schatz. It was

designed to function in the same way as a fuzee. That is, it was supposed to cause an even distribution of power throughout the entire unwinding of the mainspring, correcting for the fact that the power is slightly greater as the mainspring starts to unwind than it is at the end of the wind. In theory, there is probably some justification for the device, but the fact that the manufacturer discontinued it probably indicates that it was not successful. It's also just one more thing to get out of order. The little mainspring in the barrel is subject to breakage and, unless the cover has been put on carefully, the arbor will bind against it.

If the mainspring breaks, it (1) can be replaced, or (2) a new wheel and pinion can be obtained *without* the barrel unit. There will be no loss in the timekeeping of the clock if the barrel is eliminated. If you make the replacement, you'll notice that the bent hook on the outer end of the mainspring does not attach directly to the barrel hook. An extra, loose and straight piece of spring, about 3/8" long, rests between the barrel hook and the mainspring hook. It's quite a trick to wind the little mainspring in the barrel by hand and still keep your sense of humor!

Since the inner mainspring eye easily bends away from the arbor hook, be careful not to turn the arbor backward before you replace the entire barrel unit in the movement. When the clock is wound, the little mainspring will automatically wind itself up to the proper tension.

QUESTION (18): Where should you oil the clock?

ANSWER:
The *mainspring* should be oiled with a good mainspring lubricant. The coils unwind very slowly and, if the clock is to keep good time over a period of several years, it's important that you use a lubricant that will not oxidize or become gummy. Wet the edges of the coils. A small sized artist's brush makes a good applicator, and the oil that remains on it is sufficient to oil around the inner mainspring eye, the arbor and on the inner surface of the barrel. Don't try to "soak" the mainspring. Too much oil will pour out of the barrel cover slot when it becomes turned to the bottom.

Use a good grade of clock oil on all *pivots*, remembering that too much oil is almost as bad as too little. Under no circumstances should the pivot hole oil cups be completely filled, because eventually the oil will flow out all over the plate. If you can see that there is oil just around the pivot in the hole, you've used the correct amount. Begin with the arbor holes in the *barrel* and *barrel cover*. Often ignored, these are oiled most easily before the barrel is inserted in the movement. Oil all *pivots* in both front and back plates. Place a small drop behind the *ratchet wheel*, in the *hole of the click* and at the point where the click spring touches the click. The *anchor pin* should be oiled only slightly at the place where it touches the fork tines. If so much oil is put on that it joins the space between the pin and the tines, it will eventually run down the pin and all over the anchor. Finally, barely touch two or three of the *escape wheel teeth tips* with a very small amount of oil. Eventually a thin film will become distributed over every tooth tip as well as on the locking and impulse surfaces of the pallets. Here, too, a small sized artist's brush in a useful tool for oiling the anchor pin and escapement. The hairs of the brush should be barely "wet".

Do not oil any of the wheels and pinions in the movement. None is needed.

Do not oil the wheels and pinions of the motion train, unless the intermediate wheel has a steel arbor and pinion with one pivot in the plate and the other in a bridge. These two pivots should be oiled.

Ball pendulums should not be oiled anywhere. Disc pendulums should be oiled in the places where the regulating rod enters the two little weights.

QUESTION (19): Can 400-Day Clock parts of different manufacture be interchanged?

ANSWER:
Certain 400-Day Clock parts are interchangeable, and others can be made interchangeable with only minor alteration. However, it would be practically impossible to prepare a list of such parts which would be of any value to the repairman. There have been more than a dozen German manufacturers and assemblers of 400-Day Clocks, many of whom made more than one size movement. There are also hundreds of thousands of old clocks still in running order, whose movements were made by manufacturers no longer in existence.

The only practical procedure, therefore, is to list some of the more frequently needed replacement parts which are interchangeable, or which can be made interchangeable.

The main advantage in knowing about the interchangeability of parts is that you can procure satisfactory replacements without delay. The cost of replacement parts does not vary much from manufacturer to manufacturer, for the chief cost is in the handling. When ordering parts (See page 169), delivery may be speeded if you specify original or *comparable substitute.*

A partial list of interchangeable parts follows:

Domes: Domes of these sizes will fit the clocks of two or more manufacturers: 4 5/8" x 8", 5 1/2" x 7 5/8", 5 1/2" x 10 1/2", 7" x 12", 7 1/2" x 16". The original German domes are of very clear glass, but are slightly more costly than those that have recently been manufactured in the U.S. The domestic product, made by several glass manufacturers, varies between good and bad, the latter having window glass waviness and visible cooling rings. It's a good idea to examine the domestic dome to make sure that you are getting one that is clear, but if you are ordering by mail, it is well worth the small additional investment to specify the imported.

Some sizes of plastic domes began to make their appearance in 1955. The domestic product is of rather poor quality, but cheap. The imported product costs about the same as glass, but is clearer throughout. All plastic domes require particular care, for they are quite easily scratched.

Bases: Many standard size bases are interchangeable, but many appear to be so that are not. The important points to note are (1) the distance between the pillar post holes, (2) the diameter of these holes, (3) the position of the pendulum guide cup hole if such a hole is required, (4) the type of pendulum locking device, if any, and (5) the type of leveling screws, if any. Painted bases, particularly those with floral designs, are often difficult to match for color, even though the base itself may be of the right size. The color of the paint was not always kept constant from one batch to the next.

Suspension Blocks and Forks: It can be seen in Section 5 that there is quite a variety of sizes and shapes of suspension blocks and forks. What these illustrations do not show is that there is also variation in their thickness. Nevertheless, almost any block or fork can be substituted for another of comparable size. Three things should be noted, and if necessary, corrected. (1) The top block must be free in its saddle so that the suspension spring will pull straight from the holding screw or pin, rather than from the bottom of the block, as it will if the block is tight. (2) The length of the suspension spring between the bottom of the top block and the top of the fork must be the same as the original. (3) The bottom block and pin must be of the correct thickness, so that the pendulum can

33

be hooked and unhooked with ease, thus ruling out the possibility of bending the suspension spring.

If the top block is too thick for the saddle, or if the bottom block is too thick for the pendulum hook, make the alteration by filing the saddle or hook slots wider. Under no circumstances should you attempt to bend them open, for they will break very easily.

Pendulums: Standard clock pendulums are interchangeable with these possible variations: (1) If there is a pendulum guide cup in the base, a pendulum with an extended axis should be used. (2) The length and strength of the suspension spring must be tailored to the requirements of the substitute pendulum. (3) The pendulum hook may not fit easily over the bottom suspension block, in which case the alteration must be made as described in the preceding paragraph.

Dials: Few complete dial units are interchangeable because of the difference in the position of the three dial holding lugs. However, the dials themselves are often interchangeable as are some bezels. Before substituting an enameled dial, pay particular note to the curvature of the dial plate. If it is more convex than the original, it may not be possible for the hour hand bushing to fit over the end of the hour wheel pipe.

If a substitute dial or bezel appears to be just slightly loose, it can be cemented in position with miracle cement. Such a large variety of dials are available that it might be possible, if the original type is not immediately available, to substitute another type which will be acceptable to the customer.

Mainsprings: It is not absolutely necessary for a replaced mainspring to have the exact specifications as the original. A slight variation is possible. Four standard sizes are available which will fit practically all new and old standard size movements: 20mm x 38mm, 19mm x 38mm, 19mm x 36mm and 18mm x 38mm. (See page 163) Very little interchanging of mainsprings for miniature clocks is possible, because the barrels are not at all uniform.

Suspension Springs: The substitute suspension spring must have the same torsion characteristics as the original although the width and thickness dimensions need not be the same. One of the purposes of this Guide is to make easy the correct selection of a spring that will not only provide correct torsion, but will also make the clock keep good time. (See Section 5, and page 160)

Escape Wheels and Anchors: Substitution of both escape wheel and anchor in standard clocks for those of another manufacturer is possible with certain reservations. However, unless you have been schooled in the escapement, you probably should not attempt it. The substitution is most practical in the case of old movements for which spare parts are no longer available. It is best to exchange both anchor and escape wheel, with their arbors, so that exact alignment of pallets and wheel teeth will be assured. Also, the anchor should be of the adjustable pallet type. Since the diameters of the pivot holes of the substitute parts may differ from the originals, you may have to open or close the pivot holes. Finally, you should measure and compare the escape wheel pinion with the original. If the difference in their diameters is very great, the pinion cannot be used unless the pivot holes are altered to provide a workable distance between the pinion and the centerwheel.

Wheels, Pinions, Barrels, Plates, Arches, Suspension Brackets and Saddles: Only limited interchangeability is possible.

QUESTION (20): *What do you do when in a brand new, correctly set up clock, (1) the pendulum touches the base, (2) you've shortened the suspension spring to correct for this, and (3) you still can't get the pendulum to swing slowly enough? Should you then try a thinner spring?*

ANSWER:
No. You would just be piling error on error. Such a clock is probably one of several on the market which had either (1) thin, brass rings at the top and bottom of the columns holding the movement platform, or (2) a thin movement holding platform. In shipping, the column rings may have telescoped, thus lowering the movement just enough to make the pendulum touch the base; or, if the platform is thin and has become bent, the movement may be leaning backward, a condition which will also lower the pendulum.

If the rings have telescoped, you'd better replace them, for it's practically impossible to straighten them and still have them look right. You can prevent thin rings from telescoping again by inserting some common iron washers inside of them, so that the pressure from the tightened bolt will act upon the washers rather than upon the rings. In newer clocks, the rings are made of heavier gauge brass. These will not telescope.

You can usually straighten a slightly bent platform with hand pressure, using the movement as a lever. Be sure that your effort is directed on the plates, not on the dial or arch, for these may bend or break. Also, be sure that all of your effort is directed at the platform and not at the bottom of the columns where they join the base. When the movement is straight again, draw up firmly on the nuts under the base.

If you have shortened the suspension spring too much, you'll have to replace it with one of correct strength and length.

QUESTION (21): *How can you diagnose the fault when an apparently well-ordered clock still fails to run?*

ANSWER:
If the movement has been well cleaned and oiled, and otherwise appears to be in order, make these eight tests:

(1) Check the pendulum beat. (See Question 6.) Perhaps the suspension spring has become slightly twisted without your having noticed it.

(2) Examine the fork to see whether it is too tight, or, perhaps, too loose, on the anchor pin. (See Question 4.) The tines may be bent, and although they're apparently the right distance apart at the end, they may close up at the point where they touch the pin. If the tines are too open, much of the power from the mainspring will be dissipated. There should be *only* enough clearance to insure that the tines will never grip the pin *in any position* of its movement.

(3) Examine the anchor pin to see that it is tight. (See Question 5.) Some pins are threaded into the anchor; others are driven in and held by friction. If it is not obvious which condition prevails, try screwing the pin home before attempting to drive it in.

   If the pin is of the type that's purposely offset to bring the top portion *nearer* to the suspension spring, it will probably be found to be threaded. However, the tightening process may leave the pin in an off-center position and throw the pendulum off-beat. If it's only a few degrees off, compensate for it by adjusting the pendulum beat. However, if it's way off center, it would be best to stake the pin in its correct position.

(4) Remove the suspension unit to see if the ends of the suspension spring have been set *exactly* in the center of both the top and bottom blocks. If the spring is at all kinked between the fork and top block, you should replace it; if kinked between fork and bottom block, try to straighten it.

(5) Check the top suspension block in its saddle to be sure that it doesn't bind or is not too loose. The block should be free so that the pendulum will hang from the holding screw or pin, rather than from the bottom of the block. If the block is so loose that it moves when the anchor pin activates the suspension fork, it will absorb part of the power all of which should be directed at the pendulum.

(6) Note whether the suspension spring is touching the guard holding screws or suspension guard at any point. Also note whether the fork is touching the suspension bracket.

(7) Look through the movement, particularly at the area directly behind the back plate, to see whether the ends of any screws are touching moving parts. In some movements, the screw holding the ratchet wheel bridge has the same head and thread as the pillar screws, but is shorter. The longer screw may have been interchanged and is pressing against the barrel. Also, the lower guard holding screw, if tightened without the guard on, may be pressing against the barrel.

(8) Wait until the clock stops of its own accord. Then, carefully start the pendulum rotating again, *without touching the hands.* (The slightest movement of the hands may temporarily release a "catch".) Then note whether:

(A) The pallets hang between two teeth without touching them,(which means that there is no power from the escape wheel). If they do, remove the hands, dial and motion train (hour wheel, intermediate wheel, and cannon pinion). If the clock will run properly without them, the problem can be located somewhere within the motion train. (See Questions 13 and 14. Also, make sure that the hour hand is far enough onto the hour wheel pipe so that it cannot touch the minute hand bushing.) If the clock still won't run with the motion train removed, you know that the problem must lie between the plates.

Actually there can only be about four causes for a hung up escape wheel: (a) one or more teeth or pinion leaves are bent somewhere in the train, (b) an arbor is bent, (c) a pivot is bent, or (d) pivot holes are badly worn. The front plate holes of the center wheel and escape wheel are the most usual sources of trouble, for the enlarged holes allow the tiny leaves in the escape wheel pinion to climb up on the center wheel and lock. The front plate center wheel pivot hole has been found to be too large in some of the new miniature movements.

(B) A pallet is locked to an escape wheel tooth, thus preventing the tooth from escaping. Because it may take some time before a pallet actually does lock, the clock may run satisfactorily for a period of time.

A locked pallet is usually the result of a bent escape wheel tooth or worn pivot holes, (either the anchor or escape wheel pivot holes or both). What happens is that, because the enlarged holes allow the anchor and escape wheel to get out of position, the proper distance between them cannot be maintained and they lock together. This is one of the more tantalizing problems that arise, because the locking may occur only infrequently and rarely at a time when you are actually observing it.

One way to check on this condition is to turn the movement upside down and, with your finger pressing upward on the anchor arbor, allow the anchor to flip back and forth so that at least two or three complete turns of the escape wheel are made. This procedure brings escape wheel and anchor as closely together as possible, so if they are going to catch at all, you'll feel it with your finger. This is also a good test to check on a possible bent escape wheel tooth.

(C) The escapement seems to function properly, while, at the same time, the escape wheel teeth drop sluggishly on the pallets, with no audible snap. This condition is customarily found in clocks which have not been cleaned for a while and are loaded with old, gummy oil. However, since we are presuming that the clock has been thoroughly cleaned and oiled, the problem is to locate the cause of the power loss.

A gummy mainspring, for example, will cause as much loss of power as gummy pivot holes. If the mainspring was replaced in the barrel by hand, the chances are that its coils were seriously distorted. It is almost impossible to insert a 400-Day Clock mainspring in its barrel by hand without distorting its coils. Such distortion causes the edges of the mainspring coils to scrape the sides of the barrel as it unwinds, thus using up a large portion of its power. This can be checked by removing the mainspring and letting it hang by its outer end. If the sides of the spring are not exactly parallel, you know that it has been distorted. The only sure way of inserting the spring in the barrel properly is with a mainspring winder. (See page 166 and also the answer to Question 16.)

Loss of power can also be caused by binding of a wheel and pinion. An easy check on this is to insert the arbors between the plates two at a time, first the barrel and first wheel, then the first and second wheels, etc. Be sure to tighten all four pillars before testing each pair. Finally, insert everything between the plates except the anchor, attach the ratchet wheel, click and click spring and, with a key, give the winding arbor one quarter turn. The escape wheel should start spinning immediately. If it doesn't, either the pinions and pivots must need polishing or the pivot holes need bushings.

(D) The escapement seems to start operating properly. If, at this point, you have been unable to diagnose the cause of the stopping, it is possible that a combination of faults exist. It might be less frustrating, and certainly more economical, therefore, to substitute another movement for the present one.

There are times, particularly in old movements, when the wheels, pinions, pivot holes, pallets, etc. are so worn that to rebuild the clock would not be worth your effort. Experience has shown that the type of movement most likely to deteriorate so completely is the one having lantern pinions and pin pallet escapement. These movements have an extra wheel and pinion in the train which automatically increases the possibility of resistance, and if any one of the lantern pinions is only slightly worn or bent, it will cause a stoppage.

Since owners of old clocks wish to preserve their outward appearance, it is often practical to substitute new or good second hand movements of the same size for the old. Usually changes will be necessary only in the hand bushings, the position of the three dial lug holes in the front plate, and, possibly, the two movement holding screw holes in the platform.

QUESTION (22): I've been in the repair business over 20 years and can make a nice profit on clocks that sell for $75 or more, but I've given up taking in 400-Day Clocks. How can I make a profit when I have to cut my repair charges so much?

ANSWER:

You should not let the retail price of the clock have any influence on what your repair charge should be. In fact, you are losing a great profit opportunity by not openly soliciting 400-Day Clock repair in order to get as much of this business as possible in your area.

If you have been repairing 400-Day Clocks for a long time, you know that it takes you much less time to repair a clock now than it did when you started. You also now have your most important timesaver, *The Horolovar 400-Day Clock Repair Guide*, on your bench within easy reach. Therefore, you should have a good idea about how much of your time it will take to make a repair. So the problem boils down to how to convince your customer that a profitable charge is justified.

It's not at all unreasonable of a customer to question a repair estimate which may, in some cases, approach the original cost of the clock. But it must be explained that the clock was made in Germany by mass production, and at a labor cost considerably less than in the United States. Don't be buffaloed into cutting your charge in relation to the clock's retail price. Give a fair estimate and explain the problem carefully. Then, if the customer says he doesn't wish to pay your charge, let him walk out with the clock!

If you take in the repair at a cut rate, knowing that you are going to lose money on the job, it is only natural that you'll try to hurry the repair in order to cut your time loss to a minimum. What usually happens? You may easily make a mistake, have to re-do the job and the deal ends up taking even more of your time. Furthermore, the customer will figure that, since he was able to cut you down on this estimate, he'll try to do it again on whatever he brings in to you next.

The customer to whom you explain the economies of mass production and the German lower labor costs can only have respect for you, even though he may not agree to have you repair his clock.

Keep in mind that, possibly more than any other type of clock, the 400-Day Clock has sentimental value. Most of their owners received them as gifts. The clocks will be kept running for years to come. If you can't figure a way to make a profit on repairing them, there's a competitor nearby who can . . . and will!

QUESTION (23): Does the eccentric nut always carry the anchor pivot hole?

ANSWER:

Until recently, the eccentric nut in all 400-Day Clocks, even those made before World War I, controlled the position of the anchor pivot. However, when the very small 400-Day Clock movements began to appear in 1957 and after, some movements were made with the eccentric nut designed to carry the escape wheel pivot. In using the "trouble-shooting chart" on page 16 for making adjustments, the instruction "raise (or lower) pivot hole" refers to the anchor pivot hole. If the eccentric nut carries the escape wheel pivot, the correction made should be just opposite to that indicated.

QUESTION (24): *I've always turned the regulating nut on 400 - Day Clock pendulums clockwise to slow the clocks down. However, I've noticed that with some of the newer clocks, I have to turn counter-clockwise to slow down. This is very confusing. Can you list the plate numbers of the clocks in the Guide with pendulums having regulating nuts that must be turned* counter-clockwise *to make them go* slower ?

ANSWER:

It is impossible to furnish such a list because many manufacturers made both types of pendulums, yet gave no corresponding indication of the change on the back plates. Although the pendulum, in each case, was redesigned to eliminate play in the regulation, the regulating nut could just as well have been designed to turn in the usual way . . . *clockwise to make the clock go slower.* Why it wasn't, is one of those mysteries of foreign manufacturing.

Incidentally, it's always a good idea to explain to the customer that, if he expects the clock to keep good time, he must give it final regulation in his home. Show him the pendulum regulating nut and tell him which way it should be turned to make the clock go faster or slower. Make note on the repair ticket of the correct direction at the time you are regulating the clock.

QUESTION (25): *Are there any special instructions for the repair of the Schatz* 1000-Day *Clock?*

ANSWER:

No. The clock should be treated exactly the same as the Schatz miniature 400-Day Clock. Actually, the only major differences in basic construction between these two Schatz movements are in the barrel, which is larger; the mainspring which is longer and heavier; and the first wheel which is more heavily constructed. Also, the anchor in the Schatz 1000-Day movement has a longer arbor, because the plates are farther apart than they are in the Miniature 400-Day movement. Otherwise, most of the parts in the two types of Schatz movements are interchangeable.

QUESTION (26): *What strength Horolovar suspension spring should be used for the little 8-Day Staiger torsion pendulum clock?*

ANSWER:

The correct strength Horolovar spring is .0017" (.043mm). It's not easy to make a suspension spring replacement in this clock, because the top and bottom suspension fittings are pinched onto the ends of the spring rather than attached with screws. If possible, it's better to obtain a complete new suspension unit from one of the importers of this clock.

QUESTION (27): *I have a clock in the shop (Plate 1087), which I have cleaned and checked over carefully, It runs perfectly when the hands are off, but with the hands on, the clock always stops when both minute and hour hands are being raised. Can you suggest where the loss of power might be?*

ANSWER:

The clock you have is probably the one made by Edgar Henn Company which is covered with a glass sided case. One lot of this model clock, probably numbering several thousand, was originally made with hands which were too heavy for the movement. You can either replace the hands with lighter ones, or substitute a shorter pair without harming the appearance of the clock. Unfortunately, the Henn Company went out of business in 1956, and none of their own substitute hands are available. You'll just have to find a pair that will fit.

QUESTION (28): *My biggest problem is not with the clock. It's with their owners! They take the clock home without knowing how to set it up, they bend the spring which throws the pendulum out of beat, then they bring it back complaining that it wasn't repaired right! How can I convince them that it was their fault?*

ANSWER:

You can be sure that your customers are not any happier to have to return the clocks to you than you are to see the clocks come back! So, the problem is not one of how to convince these people that it's their fault. It's a matter of giving the owners some basic instruction on how to handle their clocks properly and, equally importantly, how *not* to abuse them.

Here is our suggestion for a solution: Before turning a 400-Day Clock over to its owner, ask him if he knows how to set it up and regulate it properly. If he says "yes," tell him you'd like to review a few points with him to be sure he knows what your guarantee includes and what it doesn't. Most likely he'll welcome anything you can tell him, because there's a fairly good chance that the only information he's ever had about the clock came from the printed instructions he received when he bought it. Unfortunately, these were not too complete!

Here, then, is a set of general instructions which you can use with every repair that you are prepared to guarantee. Permission is given to any repairman to copy and distribute these instructions, providing the clocks for which they are to be used are equipped with a HOROLOVAR TEMPERATURE COMPENSATING SUSPENSION SPRING.

Note that there are several places in which alternate instructions are given, a procedure made necessary because of the many different models in existence. You should assist your customer by checking the paragraphs which specifically apply to the clock in question.

400-DAY CLOCK REPAIR WARRANTY

With Operating Instructions

Ticket No. _____ Date _____

IDENTIFICATION

This is a _____ 400-Day Clock and has
  (Fill in name of manufacturer or name on back plate)
Back Plate No. _____ as illustrated in THE HOROLOVAR 400-DAY CLOCK REPAIR GUIDE

WARRANTY

This clock has been expertly repaired by _____

and is guaranteed against any mechanical failure, not caused by abuse, for a period of 12 months following the above date.

OWNER PLEASE NOTE

The most vital part of this clock is the thin wire "spring" from which the pendulum is suspended. It is only a little thicker than a human hair and must be treated with great care so that it does not become twisted or bent. Your clock has been equipped with a

HOROLOVAR TEMPERATURE COMPENSATING SUSPENSION SPRING

which is the best and toughest spring available. It should last forever under normal service and strains, but it will not stand abuse.

To get the most satisfaction and enjoyment from your clock, the person in charge of it should carefully review the operating instructions as given on the following pages. I have checked the paragraphs that apply to your clock.

Per _____

To Lock and Unlock the Pendulum Suspension (Read checked paragraph A or B)

Before the pendulum is put into motion, which is the way the clock is started, it is necessary to get it into a free-suspended position.

NOTES TO REPAIRMAN:

(A) Clocks With Detached Pendulums And With Suspension Spring Guards That Can Be Locked

These protection pieces, or guards, all located at the back of the movement, have different designs. Some just cover the pin block attached to the lower end of the suspension spring; others actually clamp the pin block so it can't be moved. The guard itself may be held in place friction-tight, or by a thumb-screw. Whatever the design, this protection device must be raised out of the suspension unit, and kept out of the way.

CHECK A OR B

With the lower part of the suspension unit thus exposed, the pendulum should then be very carefully hooked on. Attaching the pendulum to the suspension spring unit (and detaching it when necessary) is a most important operation, and great care must be taken not to bend the spring even the least bit! Don't try to do it with one hand. It's best to hold the little pin block in position with a finger of one hand while "hooking" the pendulum on it with the other. (When removing the pendulum from the pin block, remember that the pendulum "hook" has to be raised slightly before it can be eased off the pin.)

(B) Clocks With Attached Pendulums And With Pendulum Locking Devices (Read Checked Paragraphs C, D or E)

IF B IS CHECKED, CHECK C, D, OR E

(C) Kundo Clock

The pendulum locking lever is in the back, under the movement. A "safety" cotter pin may be in position (to prevent the lever from opening accidentally during shipping) and this pin must be removed before the locking lever can be opened. (If the clock has been factory packed, a brass clamp may be attached to the upper part of the pendulum. It should be pulled off and discarded.) The pendulum should be carefully held, when the locking lever is pushed to the side, allowing it to be lowered gently into the free position: a drop of about 1/8".

CAUTION: When this action is reversed - that is, when the pendulum is to be locked again for moving or shipping - remember that it must be carefully raised (about 1/8") into its socket so that the locking lever will hold it in a firm position. If you pull the locking lever over without first raising the pendulum into its socket, no locking takes place. In such case, the suspension spring is quite likely to be seriously bent if the clock is tipped.

If the clock is to be shipped, it is advisable to replace the "safety" pin in the hole by the lever. A satisfactory pin can be made from a slightly-opened paper clip, if the original cotter pin that came with the clock is not available. (If no hole for a "safety" pin is provided, the locking lever should be held in the locked position with a rubber band or string.)

(D) Schatz Clock

The pendulum of this clock is locked and unlocked by a lever which is located in front of the clock, at the bottom of the base. When the lever is moved to an extreme right position, the pendulum is raised and locked; when it is moved to the extreme left position, the pendulum is lowered and is "free."

A second and more secure pendulum lock is provided for use when the clock is shipped. This lock is at the back of the movement, located in the lower unit of the tubular suspension spring guard. This lower guard unit can be adjusted - either locked (lowered) or unlocked (raised) - by means of a thumb screw. Except when the clock is being shipped, this adjustable guard unit should be raised as high as it will go, and held there by tightening the thumb screw.

To lock the pendulum for shipping, loosen the thumb screw and lower the unit in such a way that the two prongs provided not only go through the two holes in the pendulum locking bracket, but also through two more holes in the disc at the top of the pendulum. (It may be necessary to rotate the pendulum slightly to find a pair of matching holes through which the prongs will pass.) When the two prongs of the unit have thus been fully seated, the thumb screw should be tightened to hold the guard unit in place.

(E) Other Clocks

There are many different types of pendulum locking mechanisms, most of which provide some means of raising the pendulum against a bracket, at the rear of the movement, thereby supporting the pendulum at top and bottom during shipping. If the method of operating the mechanism on your clock is not clear, read the instructions in the paragraphs above which explain other types of locking devices. If they don't help you to determine how yours works, take the clock to your local clock repairman who will be glad to explain the operation to you.

To Place The Clock

The clock should be placed in a position free from vibration. Television sets, pianos, unsteady bookcases or tables are all unsatis-

To Regulate The Clock (Read checked paragraphs F or G)

If the clock is to be used as a timepiece, it should be carefully regulated.

(F) On disc pendulums of some pre-World War I clocks, there are two little weights which can be moved, by turning a threaded steel rod with a key, either toward the center of the pendulum (turn key toward F or A to make the clock go faster), or away from the center (turn key toward S or R to make the clock go slower). (A double-end key - for both regulating and winding - is made for this clock which is available from your clockmaker.)

CHECK
F OR G

(G) On 3-ball and 4-ball pendulums of later models, a round, knurled regulating "nut" (about the size of a quarter) is at the top. When turned, it will make the balls go toward, or away from, the center of the pendulum. The direction in which the regulating nut should be turned to make the clock go faster or slower depends upon the design of the pendulum. Look for the letters "F" (fast) and "S" (slow) on top of or near the pendulum nut.

To make this clock go SLOWER:

    (H) Turn regulating nut to the right (clockwise)

    (I) Turn regulating nut to the left (counterclockwise)

IF G IS
CHECKED,
CHECK H
OR I

To Adjust For Accurate Timekeeping

The most practical way of regulating the clock is as follows: At least a half-hour after the clock has first been set up and started, at which time the pendulum should be rotating back and forth at its normal rate, set the hands to some accurate source of time such as an electric clock. Cover the clock with its dome or case and don't touch it again for a week.

At the end of the week, compare the time with the accurate time source and note the number of minutes that the clock has run fast or slow. To correct its rate of gain or loss, stop the pendulum at the point where it reverses its cycle, and adjust the regulating nut (or regulating rod on old clocks) as described above. Then, release the pendulum at, or just a little beyond, the place where you stopped it. (By making the regulating adjustment while holding the pendulum at one end of its cycle, you avoid overswinging it when you start it again. An overswing negatively affects accurate regulation.) Reset the hands to the correct time, and let the clock run without further correction for another week.

Be sure to make a note of the amount the clock ran fast or slow, and the amount of turn you gave the regulating nut (or key), 1/4 turn, 1/8 turn, etc. When you compare the original gain or loss for the following week, you'll know whether you are approaching the timekeeping limits of the clock. After a few weeks of regulation, you will

---

factory places. A mantel, a sturdy piece of furniture, or even a wall bracket, is to be preferred. It will not help its timekeeping qualities if the clock is placed directly over a radiator, or in a window where it will be subjected to direct sunlight or to drafts.

To Level The Clock

Even though the surface on which the clock rests need not be completely level, the clock itself must be level. But you don't need a leveling tool! It is easy to level a clock which is provided with a pendulum guide cup on the base, directly under the pendulum. The clock is level when the bottom of the pendulum is over the middle of the cup.

For an older clock, not provided with a pendulum guide cup on the base, the clock can be leveled by eye. As you face the front of the clock, the vertical axis of the pendulum should be directly along an imaginary line sighted from the figure 12 down through the figure 6 on the dial. As you look from the side of the clock, the pendulum suspension spring should be parallel to the movement's back plate.

If the base of the clock is provided with leveling screws, any leveling correction can be made by raising or lowering one or more of these screws. If leveling screws are not provided, the correction can be made by inserting one or more pieces of stiff cardboard under the edge of the base in two places (to prevent wobbling).

To Start The Clock - Very Important!

Carefully rotate the pendulum, either to the left or right, so that it is one complete turn from dead center, then release it. This will start the pendulum rotating about two complete turns - more than is usually required. Depending upon the clock, the normal rotation may be as little as 3/4 of a turn or as much as almost 2 turns. After the pendulum has continued to rotate for a half hour or so, it will have "settled down" to its normal cycle. Once you know how far the pendulum normally rotates in one direction, always give it just the amount of rotation, plus a half inch or so more, whenever you have to start it. Never rotate the pendulum more than one full turn from dead center. If you do, a permanent twist may be left in the suspension spring which will prevent the clock from running. (No clock repairman can be expected to replace a suspension spring, free of charge, if the spring has been permanently twisted or otherwise bent.)

To Set The Hands

Set the time by moving the minute hand in either direction. The hour hand will automatically follow. If the hour hand does not point exactly to the hour when the minute hand is at 12, rotate it, in either direction (it's on friction-tight), until it does point to the hour. Don't be alarmed if the escapement "flutters" when the hands are moved while the clock is running.

reach a point when a 1/8" turn of the regulating nut will change the timing from fast to slow (or from slow to fast). At this point, you've reached the maximum possible regulation. Do not make any further regulating adjustments unless the clock is moved to a different position. Don't expect the clock to keep accurate time permanently! Every couple of weeks, or whenever necessary, reset the hands to the correct time.

While the clock is designed to run for more than 400 days on one winding, it will keep much better time if it is wound every six months.

To Wind The Clock

When fully wound, the 400-Day Clock will usually run for 500 or more days. However, many people like to make a ceremony of the winding operation by doing it once a year on birthdays, wedding anniversaries, etc. All 400-Day Clocks, which are wound from the back of the movement, wind to the left - counterclockwise. The mainspring is a heavy one and a little pressure is needed to turn the key. It is impossible to overwind the clock, so keep turning the key until the spring is obviously wound tight. (Hint: The clock will keep more accurate time throughout the year if it is wound every six months.)

To Keep The Key Handy

One of the best places to keep the key, so that it will be available when the winding takes place, is right under the clock!

To Clean Glass or Plastic Covers

Most clocks are covered with glass or plastic domes, or by glass or plastic sided cases. The clocks are most attractive when the glass or plastic is kept clean and bright.

Glass Domes Wash occasionally in very hot water and wipe off with a clean, dry towel. The dome can be kept bright over long periods by just wiping it off with a clean, damp, paper towel while it is on the clock. When removing the dome from the clock, always grip it as near to the bottom as possible. This will keep your fingerprints in an area where they won't show.

Glass Sided Cases Wipe both sides with a soft cloth, wrung out with hot water. Wipe off with a clean, soft, dry towel. Do not dip the case in water. The sides can be kept bright over long periods by wiping occasionally with a clean, dry cloth while the case is on the clock. Avoid putting your fingers on the glass when removing the case.

Plastic Domes or Cases Follow the same instructions as above, but avoid extremely hot water. Always use a very soft cloth when wiping. Plastic is relatively soft and will eventually become dull if wiped repeatedly with a rough cloth.

QUESTION (29): How can you identify a genuine Horolovar suspension spring?

ANSWER:
Although there are many imitation springs on the market, some of which appear upon casual examination to be exactly the same as Horolovar, a genuine Horolovar spring can be determined by measuring its width. Fortunately, no other spring manufacturer has used the same width, for otherwise it would be impossible to identify the genuine product without a chemical analysis. All Horolovar springs have the same width: .0162" (.411mm). Horolovar springs are never sold in bulk. Each is packaged in an individual compartment in a three-color envelope - red, black and white - with the name HOROLOVAR TEMPERATURE COMPENSATING prominently displayed.

It is important to remember that, if you are following suspension spring strength (thickness) recommendations in the Horolovar Repair Guide, Horolovar suspension springs are the only ones which will allow you to regulate the clock within the regulating limits of the pendulum.

QUESTION (30): Is it possible to tighten the two movement holding screws too much?

ANSWER:
Yes, it is possible to tighten the screws on some clocks so much that the movement pillars will bend. This, in turn, will pull the lower part of the plates together, which may eliminate the end play required for the barrel and first wheel arbors, and stop the clock. Thus, care should be taken not to draw the movement holding screws up so tight. Since the only function of these two screws is to keep the movement from falling off of its support, a firm turn with pliers is sufficient. Some manufacturers have placed spacer washers under the pillars to prevent them from becoming distorted when the movement holding screws are tightened. This is an acceptable refinement, but is not really a necessary one.

QUESTION (31): How can I tell where to put the fork on a suspension spring unit that is not illustrated in the Guide?

ANSWER:
When the position of the fork on the suspension spring is not known for an old clock, you'll have

to find the correct position by trial and error. Begin by attaching the fork so that there is about 1/4" between the top of the fork and the bottom of the top block. If, with the fork in this position, the anchor "flutters," raise the fork slightly. If the anchor moves with a "jerky" motion, lower the fork slightly. You will find a position in between these extremes that will be correct, assuming, of course, that the escapement is in good order.

QUESTION (32): I have a Horolovar Mainspring Winder which does a good job of winding a spring into the barrel, but how do I get it out?

ANSWER:
Without the use of elaborate and expensive equipment, a simple and satisfactory method is this: with a pair of offset pliers in one hand, grip one or two of the inner coils of the mainspring. Hold the barrel with the other hand in such a way that you can wind up the spring inside of the barrel as much as possible. Then, quickly yank the spring out of the barrel. For safety, use gloves and drop a cloth over your hands so that the spring can not fly in your face. When you remove the spring from the barrel this quickly while it is under slight tension, you will find that no distortion will occur.

QUESTION (33): Why can't I get 400-Day Clock parts from my jobber as fast as I can get watch parts?

ANSWER:
While most alert jobbers will carry Horolovar suspension springs and other Horolovar clock repair aids in stock, it is not practical or profitable for the average jobber to carry 400-Day Clock spare parts. For, while there is a constant demand for the thousands of different parts carried by The Horolovar Company, the demand for any one particular part from the jobber would be very small.

QUESTION (34): Will Horolovar suspension springs fit old torsion pendulum battery clocks?

ANSWER:
The .0045" (.114mm) Horolovar spring will operate perfectly with the small "Tiffany Never Wind" torsion pendulum clocks. These clocks go by several different names including "The Tiffany Electric Manufacturing Co.," "Never Wind," "Cloister Clock Co.," "Cloister," and "Niagara Clock Co." This size clock is covered with a glass dome, 4 5/8" in diameter and about 8" high. There is a larger model "Tiffany" covered with a 6 1/2" diameter dome about 10" high, for which no Horolovar 400-Day Clock spring is strong enough.

QUESTION (35): To make a clock go slower, should I use a stronger or weaker spring?

ANSWER:
Use a weaker spring.

QUESTION (36): I find it impossible to adjust the escapement on some clocks so that the anchor pin will go absolutely smoothly from one side to the other. How can a jerk be eliminated?

ANSWER:
If the jerk is very slight, don't try to eliminate it. This minor backlash is perfectly normal with many clocks. Here's what's happening:

Near the end of the pendulum's rotation, the suspension spring is twisted sufficiently to cause the fork to move the anchor far enough to allow an escape tooth to be released from a pallet. The tooth drops high on the opposite pallet and, almost immediately thereafter, the pendulum reverses its rotation. During this reverse cycle, the spring untwists, and the fork guides the anchor back. The pallet pulls away from the escape tooth until the tooth engages the pallet's impulse surface. The resulting impulse given to the anchor causes a slight forward twist to the spring which is what keeps the pendulum in motion. When the escape tooth finally drops off of the pallet, the fork immediately assumes its position on the spring without interference. It is at this point that there may be a slight, momentary backlash of the anchor pin.

In short, the minor backlash is merely a repositioning of the fork by the spring after the escape tooth has ceased its impulse action. Don't confuse this action with "fluttering" which is covered in the answer to Question 3.

SECTION **3** . . . NAMES AND TRADE MARKS ON DIALS

Although this Guide deals primarily with names and trade marks found on back plates, certain names and trade marks are also occasionally found on dials. The following list identifies most of the dial names which will be seen.

Adoria	Appears on some dials of the pre-World War I Schatz clocks. (See Schatz)
American Specialty Co.	Pre-World War I U. S. importer, New York.
Anniversary	Trade mark copyrighted in 1901 by Bowler & Burdick Co., Cleveland, Ohio, who applied the name to all 400-Day Clocks imported by them.
Annual	Appears on some dials of Kieninger & Obergfell, German manufacturer.
Bentima	Trade mark of an English importer and appears on clocks manufactured by Kern & Sohne, Germany.
Birks	Appears on some dials of Kieninger & Obergfell, German manufacturer.
Bucherer	Appears on some dials of Konrad Mauch, German manufacturer.
BuK	Appears on some dials of Kieninger & Obergfell, German manufacturer.
Black Forest	Appears on some dials of the Wurthner Company, German manufacturer.
Clebar	Appears on some dials of the Wurthner Company, German manufacturer.
Crescent	Trade mark of Ishihara Clock Co., Ltd., Japanese manufacturer.
DeBruce	Trade mark of Royce Watch Company, subsidiary of Walter Kocher Company, U. S. importer.
Dial	Appears on some dials of Uhrenfabrik Herr KG, German clock assembler.
Elvia	Appears on some dials of Kieninger & Obergfell, German manufacturer.
Eve	Appears on some dials of Walter Petersen, German manufacturer.
S. Fisher, Ltd.	Pre-World War I English retailer, London.
Forestville	Trade mark of the Forestville Clock Company, U.S. importer, New York.
Fortuna	Trade mark of a Pre-World War I German manufacturer.
4 jewels	Appears on some dials of Edgar Henn Co., German manufacturer.
Givolas, Paris	Pre-World War I French manufacturer, Paris.
Gruttert, Bremen	Appears on some dials of Kieninger & Obergfell, German manufacturer.
Gufa	Trade mark of Uhrenfabrik Gutenbacker, German clock assembler.

45

Haller or Hallers	Trade mark of Jauch & Haller Co., German manufacturer.
Heco	Trade mark of Henry Coehler Company, U. S., importer, New York.
Heirloom	Trade mark of Heirloom Clock Company, U. S. importer.
Hermle	Trade mark of Franz Hermle Co., German manufacturer.
Herr	Trade mark of Uhrenfabrik Herr KG, German clock assembler.
Jauch Haller	Trade mark of Jauch & Haller Co., German manufacturer.
Hervo	Appears on some dials of the Wurthner Company, German manufacturer.
Kaiser	Trade mark of J. Kaiser Co., German manufacturer.
Kuehl Clock Co.	Pre-World War I U. S. Importer, Chicago.
Kern	Trade mark of Kern & Sohne, German manufacturer.
Koma	Trade mark of Konrad Mauch, German manufacturer.
Kundo	Trade mark of Kieninger & Obergfell, German manufacturer.
Lepold Company	Pre-World War I U. S. importer, Chicago.
Linco	Trade mark of J. Link & Company, German manufacturer.
Louis Philipp	Appears on some dials of Kieninger & Obergfell, German manufacturer.
Master	Trade mark of Nisshin Clock Industrial Co., Ltd., Japanese manufacturer.
Montrose	Trade mark of P. R. Myers & Co., U. S. importer, Mamaroneck, N. Y.
C. D. Peacock	Pre-World War I U. S. importer, Chicago.
Perfecta	Trade mark of Perfecta Watch and Clock Co., U. S. importer, Los Angeles.
Precisa	Appears on some dials of Kieninger & Obergfell, German manufacturer.
Rensie	Trade mark of the Rensie Watch Company, U. S. importer, New York.
Schatz	Trade mark of Aug. Schatz & Sohne, German manufacturer.
Selva	Appears on some dials of Kern & Sohne, German manufacturer.
SM	Trade mark of Sokol Montag & Co., pre-World War I U. S. importer, New York.
Style King	Trade mark of Cuckoo Clock Manufacturing Company, U. S. importer, New York.
Treasureland	Appears on some dials of Kieninger & Obergfell, German manufacturer.
Urania	Trade mark of a pre-World War I German manufacturer.
John Wanamaker	Trade mark of John Wanamaker, U. S. importer, New York and Philadelphia.
Welby	Trade mark of Welby Corporation, U. S. importer, Chicago.

SECTION 4 . . . BACK PLATE ILLUSTRATIONS

Back plate markings serve as "fingerprints" which help to identify the clocks of the many manufacturers. Clocks that were originally purchased in Germany, or were imported into the U.S. prior to October 1913, could have completely blank plates or plates with just serial numbers on them. But after that date, the U.S. customs required the manufacturer to mark either his own name or the name of the U.S. importer on the plate as well as the words "Germany" or "Made in Germany." Because the name of the importer often appears above the words "Made in Germany" the importer is often thought to be the name of the manufacturer.

Some sources believe that at least some of the relatively few 400-Day Clock movements with *round* plates, especially those in brass and beveled glass cases, were made in France. However, this writer has not yet seen a 400-Day Clock movement with the words "France" or "Made in France" stamped on the back plate. Since French patents for 400-Day Clocks do exist, this could be taken to indicate just that French 400-Day Clocks were never commercially imported into the U.S. But whatever French production did exist was extremely small. Practically all 400-Day Clock movements in French type cases not specifically marked "France", were actually made in Germany, even though the wheels and pinions do have French characteristics. On the other hand, round plate movements stamped "Germany" may be seen in brass and glass cases stamped "France." The back plate from one of these movements is No. 1179.

A good many, though not all, of the clocks manufactured during the first quarter of the century had serial numbers stamped on their back plates. Since each manufacturer chose a different style or size of numeral, and since he usually stamped his serial number in about the same position on every plate, the serial number provides another clue to manufacturer identification.

It is not known exactly when serialization of 400-Day Clocks was stopped, but it probably was about 1930. There were, of course, many clocks made prior to 1930 without serial numbers.

The patent numbers D.R.P. No. 144688 and U.S.P. 751686 which appear on some back plates refer to a specially designed "twin loop" pendulum which was thought to help compensate for the effect of temperature changes on the suspension spring. This patent does not refer to any part of the movement. (Prior to the issuance of the patent, the back plate carried the words "Patent Angemeldet - Patents Applied." The U.S. patent was issued to Henrich Sattler, Munich, Germany, on February 9, 1904.) Apparently several manufacturers employed the use of this special pendulum, for the patent numbers are to be found on the back plates of different movements. However, it is quite definite that this pendulum was not always used with every clock that carried the pendulum's patent numbers.

This "temperature compensating" pendulum is only one of several different, and often complicated, types which were designed to help correct the timekeeping errors in the clock caused by changing temperature effect on the suspension spring and pendulum bob. If the Horolovar Temperature Compensating Suspension Spring had been available, such elaborate attempts to make the correction, via the pendulum, would have been unnecessary.

47

HOW TO USE THE BACKPLATE ILLUSTRATIONS

How Plates are Arranged

Plates are arranged alphabetically where there is at least one letter in the marking. Following them, at random, are plates having serial numbers only. Finally, blank plates with no names, letters or numbers are at the end.

Note that alphabetization is by the *first letter* of a name or trade mark. Thus Gustav Becker will be found in G, The National Silver Company will be in T, etc.

If there is no name or trade mark, other lettered markings are alphabetized. For instance, Made in Germany will be in M, Germany will be in G, the letters D.R.G.M. in D, etc.

About Horolovar Spring Strengths

The Horolovar spring strengths shown for each back plate are based on the assumption that the clock has its original pendulum, and that its shape, size or weight has not been altered.

An asterisk (*) following a spring size indicates that there is some question about whether the clock tested had the original pendulum.

A minus sign (-) following a spring size indicates that the required spring falls between two **HOROLOVAR** stock strengths, and the strength shown is the heavier and must be thinned down. To thin a spring, hold the pendulum firmly while, with a few strokes of a small, folded piece of fine emery cloth, you rub up and down the taut spring. Check the timing and repeat the process until the spring strength falls within the regulating range of the pendulum.

About Horolovar Mainspring Sizes

Where it has been possible, the size of the Horolovar Mainspring to use with the clock is shown by each plate: 19 x 38, 19 x 36, etc. (See page **163** for details of mainspring sizes.)

Illustrations

The *outlines* of the plates are fairly exact. The holes are *for position only*, and particularly in the case of pivot holes, are generally larger than the actual holes in the plates.

All *threaded* holes are shown in solid black.

About the Suspension Units

Complete suspension Units for clocks imported since 1949 are illustrated in Section 5, beginning on page **145** . The numbers which designate these Units are indicated under each back plate illustration: Units 1, 3A; Units 6, 7, 8, 9; Units 13: etc. When a choice of Units which can be selected for use is indicated, it is advisable to refer to the illustrations and descriptions in Section 5 in order to determine which one is best to use.

Some Units recommended are slightly different in design from the Unit originally in the clock. Always use the *recommended* Unit, for usually this is the latest one suggested by the manufacturer.

A

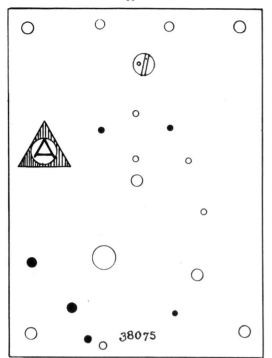

38075

Plate 1001   4-Ball Pendulum
USE .0032″ (.081mm) HOROLOVAR
Units 1, 3A   (19 x 38)

ALB. WINTERMANTEL

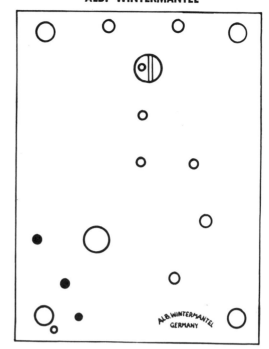

Plate 1003   Disc Pendulum
USE .0045″— (.114mm—) HOROLOVAR
                                 (19 x 36)

A M C

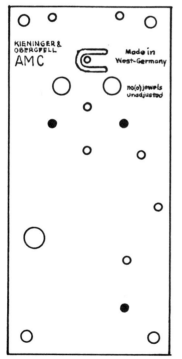

Plate 1004   4-Ball Pendulum
USE .0032″ (.081mm) HOROLOVAR
Unit 3C   (19 x 38)

A M C

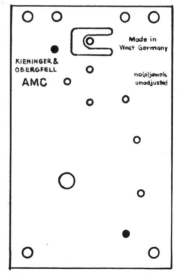

Plate 1004A   4-Ball Pendulum
USE .0023″ (.058mm) HOROLOVAR
Unit 5E
USE .0022″— (.056mm—) HOROLOVAR
Unit 5F   (14 x 30)

AMERICAN CLOCK CO.

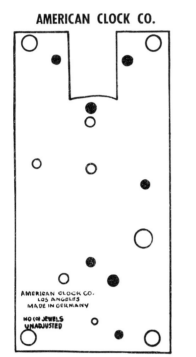

Plate 1005   4-Ball Pendulum
USE .0035″ (.089mm) HOROLOVAR
Units 13A, 13B   (20 x 38)

AMERICAN CLOCK CO.

Plate 1006   4-Ball Pendulum
                             Miniature Clock
USE .0032″ (.081mm) HOROLOVAR
Unit 14A
USE .003″ (.076mm) HOROLOVAR
Unit 14B   (13 x 32)

ANNIVERSARY

ANNIVERSARY

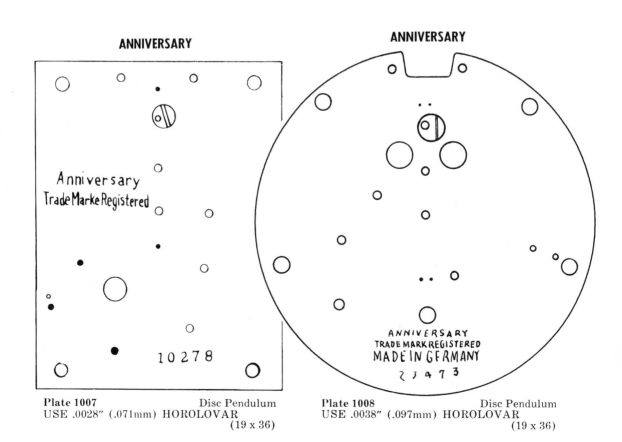

Plate 1007   Disc Pendulum
USE .0028″ (.071mm) HOROLOVAR
                      (19 x 36)

Plate 1008   Disc Pendulum
USE .0038″ (.097mm) HOROLOVAR
                      (19 x 36)

ANNIVERSARY

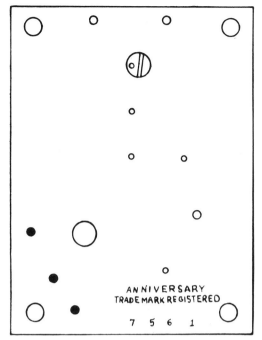

ANNIVERSARY
TRADE MARK REGISTERED

7   5   6   1

Plate 1009   Disc Pendulum
USE .004" (.102mm) HOROLOVAR
                                    (19 x 36)

ANNIVERSARY

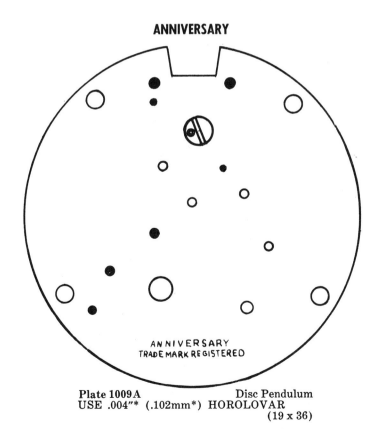

ANNIVERSARY
TRADE MARK REGISTERED

Plate 1009A   Disc Pendulum
USE .004"* (.102mm*) HOROLOVAR
                                    (19 x 36)

A. SCHATZ & SONS

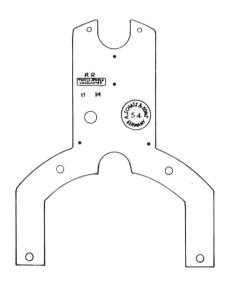

(½ actual size)

Plate 1010　　　　　4-Ball Pendulum
　　　　　　　　　　　　1000-Day Clock
USE .0024″ (.061mm) HOROLOVAR
Unit 10B　　　　　　　　(21 x 50)

A. SCHATZ & SONS

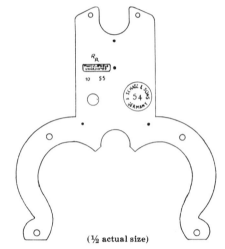

(½ actual size)

Plate 1010A
　　　　　　　　　　　4-Ball Pendulum
　　　　　　　　　　　1000-Day Clock
USE .0024″ (.061mm) HOROLOVAR
Unit 10B　　　　　　　　(21 x 50)

ASSOCIATED MERCHANDISING CORP.

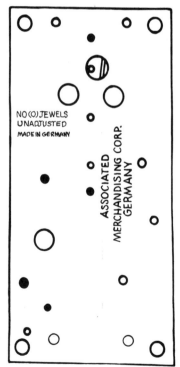

Plate 1012　　　　　4-Ball Pendulum
USE .0035″ (.089mm) HOROLOVAR
Units 19, 20A, 21
USE .0038″ (.097mm) HOROLOVAR
Unit 27B　　　　　　　　(19 x 36)

AUG. SCHATZ & SOHNE

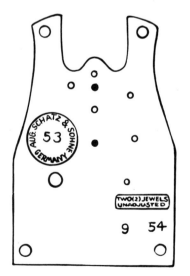

Plate 1013

　　　　Dome Clock — 3-Ball Pendulum
　　　　Coach Clock — 4-Ball Pendulum
USE .0023″ (.058mm) HOROLOVAR
Unit 10A　　　　　　　　(13 x 30)

52

AUG. SCHATZ & SOHNE

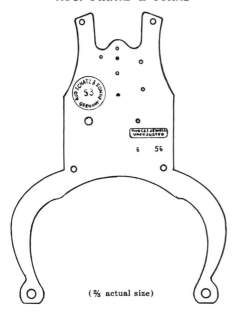

(⅔ actual size)

Plate 1013A

Dome Clock — 3-Ball Pendulum
Coach Clock — 4-Ball Pendulum
USE .0023″ (.058mm) HOROLOVAR
Unit 10 A   (13 x 30)

AUG. SCHATZ & SOHNE

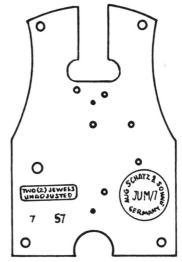

Plate 1013B

4-Ball Pendulum
Midget Clock
Pin Pallet Escapement
USE .0022″ (.056mm) HOROLOVAR
Unit 10C   (13 x 30)

AUG. SCHATZ & SOHNE

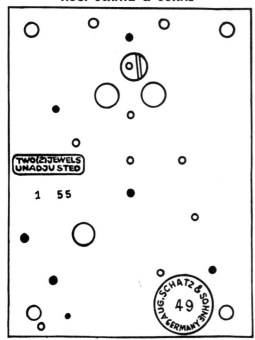

Plate 1014   4-Ball Pendulum
USE .004″ (.102mm) HOROLOVAR
Units 6, 7, 8, 9   (19 x 36)

AUG. SCHATZ & SOHNE

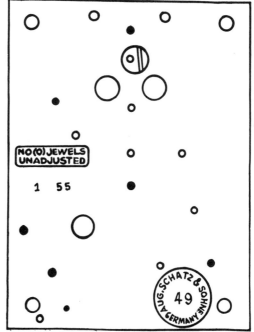

Plate 1014A   4-Ball Pendulum
USE .004″ (.102mm) HOROLOVAR
Units 6, 7, 8, 9   (19 x 36)

B

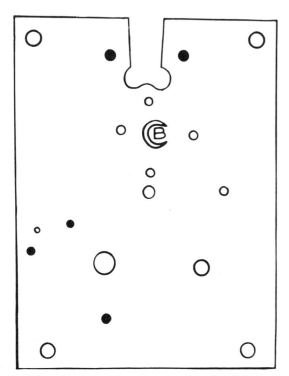

Plate 1015   Disc Pendulum
Lantern Pinions
USE .0045″— (.114mm—) HOROLOVAR
(20 x 38)

BACHMAIER-KLEMMER

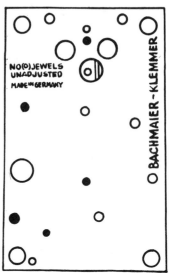

Plate 1016   Standard 4-Ball Pendulum
Miniature Movement
USE .0032″ (.081mm) HOROLOVAR
Unit 23B   (16 x 36)

BADENIA REGD.

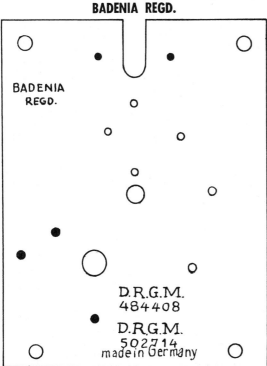

Plate 1016A   Disc Pendulum
Pin Pallet Escapement
Lantern Pinions
USE .0038″ (.097mm) HOROLOVAR
(20 x 38)

BADUF G.m.b.H.

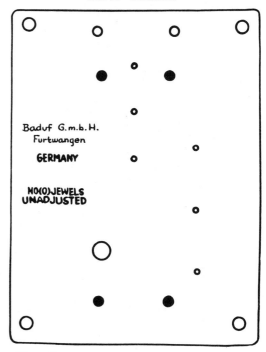

Plate 1017   4-Ball Pendulum
USE .0033″ (.084mm) HOROLOVAR
Units 18B, 18C   (19 x 38)

BAD UHRENFABRIK

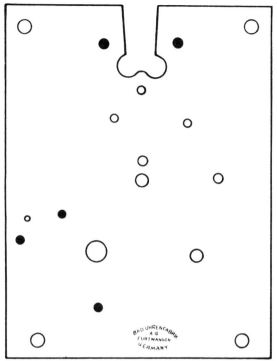

Plate 1019
3-Ball Pendulum
Lantern Pinions
USE .0035″ (.089mm) HOROLOVAR
(20 x 38)

BECKEN

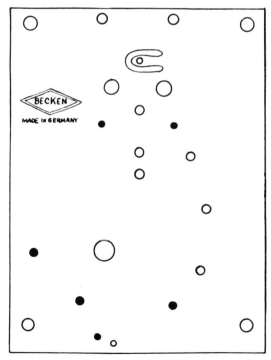

Plate 1023
4-Ball Pendulum
USE .0032″ (.081mm) HOROLOVAR
Units 1, 3A
(19 x 38)

BECKEN

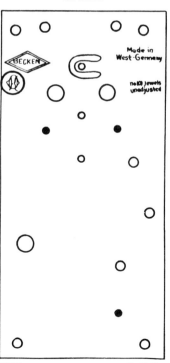

Plate 1027
4-Ball Pendulum
USE .0032″ (.081mm) HOROLOVAR
Units 1, 3A, 3B, 3C
(19 x 38)

BECKEN

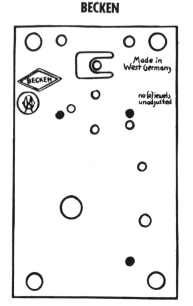

Plate 1031　　　　　4-Ball Pendulum
　　　　　　　　　　　Miniature Clock
USE .0023″ (.058mm) HOROLOVAR
Units 5A, 5B, 5C, 5D, 5E　　　(14 x 30)

BHA

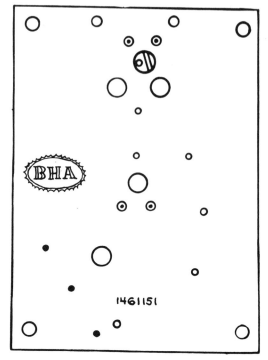

Plate 1032　　　　　Disc Pendulum
USE .004″ (.102mm) HOROLOVAR
　　　　　　　　　　　　(19 x 38)

BHA

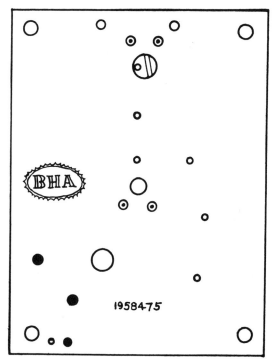

Plate 1032A　　　　　Disc Pendulum
USE .004″ (.102mm) HOROLOVAR
　　　　　　　　　　　　(19 x 38)

56

BHA

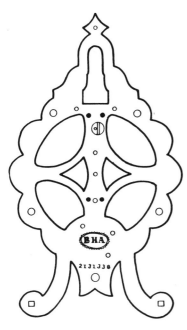

(½ actual size)

Plate 1033   Skeleton Disc Pendulum
                               Skeleton Clock
USE .004″ (.012mm) HOROLOVAR
                                   (19 x 38)

CHARLES NUNNENMAN

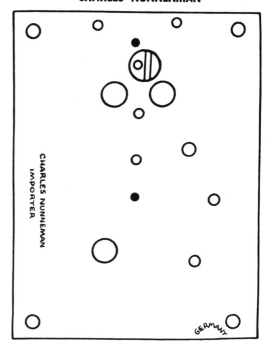

Plate 1034   4-Ball Pendulum
USE .0035″ (.089mm) HOROLOVAR
                                   (19 x 36)

COOP

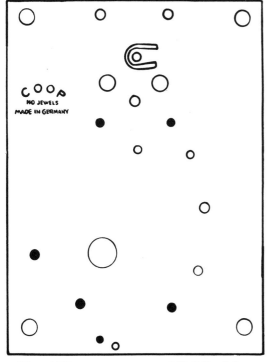

Plate 1035   4-Ball Pendulum
USE .0032″ (.081mm) HOROLOVAR
Units 1, 3A   (19 x 38)

CUCKOO CLOCK MFG. CO.

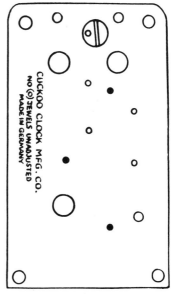

Plate 1036   4-Ball Pendulum
                              Miniature Clock
USE .0023″ (.058mm) HOROLOVAR
Units 29A, 29B   (19 x 32)

CUCKOO CLOCK MFG. CO.

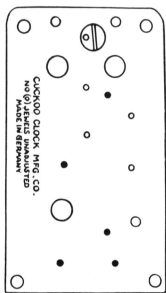

Plate 1037   4-Ball Pendulum
                             Miniature Clock
USE .0023" (.058mm) HOROLOVAR
Units 29A, 29B   (19 x 32)

CUCKOO CLOCK MFG. CO. INC.

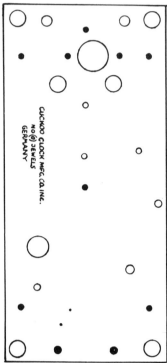

Plate 1038   4-Ball Pendulum
USE .0037" (.094mm) HOROLOVAR
Unit 32   (19 x 38)

CUCKOO CLOCK MFG. CO. INC.

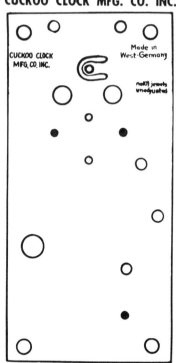

Plate 1039A   4-Ball Pendulum
USE .0032" (.081mm) HOROLOVAR
Unit 3C   (19 x 38)

CUCKOO CLOCK MFG. CO. INC.

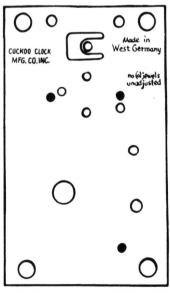

Plate 1040   4-Ball Pendulum
                            Miniature Clock
USE .0023" (.058mm) HOROLOVAR
Units 5C, 5D, 5E   (14 x 30)

CUCKOO CLOCK MFG. CO. INC.

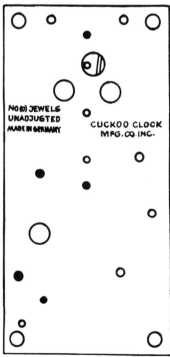

Plate 1040A   4-Ball Pendulum
USE .0035" (.089mm) HOROLOVAR
Units 19, 20A, 21
USE .0038" (.097mm) HOROLOVAR
Unit 27B   (19 x 36)

CUCKOO CLOCK MFG. CO. INC.

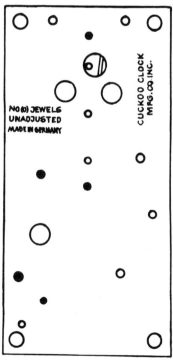

Plate 1040B   4-Ball Pendulum
USE .0035" (.089mm) HOROLOVAR
Units 19, 20A, 21
USE .0038" (.097mm) HOROLOVAR
Unit 27B   (19 x 36)

DE BRUCE WATCH CO., INC.

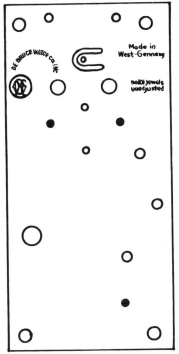

DE BRUCE WATCH CO., INC.

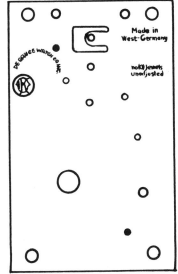

Plate 1040D   4-Ball Pendulum
USE .0023″ (.058mm) HOROLOVAR
Unit 5E
USE .0022″ — (.056mm—) HOROLOVAR
Unit 5F   (14 x 30)

Plate 1040C   4-Ball Pendulum
USE .0032″ (.081mm) HOROLOVAR
Unit 3C   (19 x 38)

DEMMLER IMPORTS

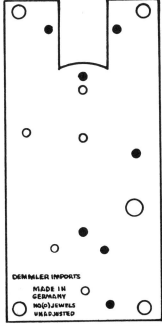

DEMMLER IMPORTS

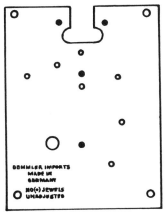

Plate 1040K   3-Ball Pendulum
                              Pin Pallet Escapement
USE .0022″ (.056mm) HOROLOVAR
Unit 38   (12 x 25)

Plate 1040H   4-Ball Pendulum
USE .0035″ (.089mm) HOROLOVAR
Units 13A, 13B   (20 x 38)

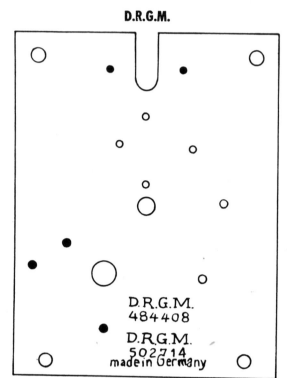

Plate 1041
D.R.G.M.
484408
D.R.G.M.
502714
made in Germany

Disc Pendulum
Pin Pallet Escapement
Lantern Pinions
USE .0038″ (.097mm) HOROLOVAR
(20 x 38)

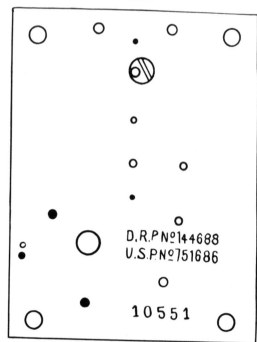

D.R.P.N°144688
U.S.P.N°751686

10551

Plate 1043
USE .004″ (.102mm) HOROLOVAR

Disc Pendulum

(19 x 36)

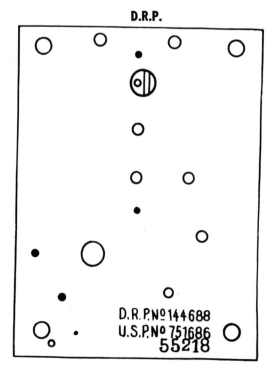

D.R.P.N°144688
U.S.P.N°751686
55218

Plate 1047
USE .0037″ (.094mm) HOROLOVAR
USE .0045″— (.114mm—) 6½″ spring
(19 x 36)

Disc Pendulum

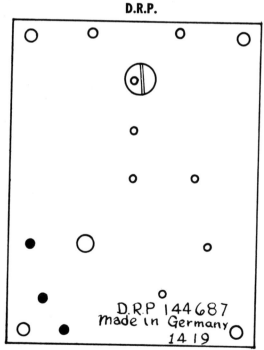

D.R.P 144687
made in Germany
1419

Plate 1049
USE .004″ (.102mm) HOROLOVAR

Disc Pendulum

(19 x 36)

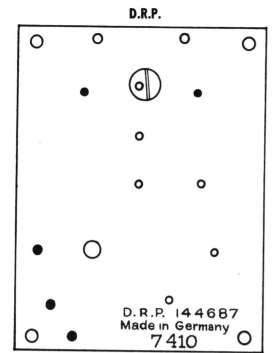

Plate Plate 1049A   Disc Pendulum
USE .004″ (.102mm) HOROLOVAR
                        (19 x 36)

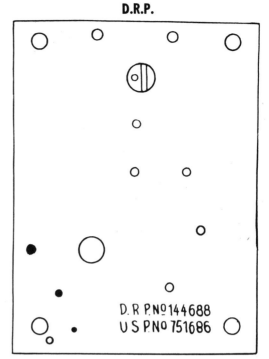

Plate 1051   Twin Loop "Temperature
Compensating" Pendulum
6¾″ Suspension Spring
USE .005″ (.127mm) HOROLOVAR
                       (19 x 36)

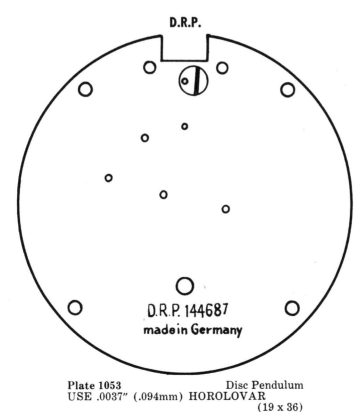

Plate 1053   Disc Pendulum
USE .0037″ (.094mm) HOROLOVAR
                     (19 x 36)

61

D.R.P.

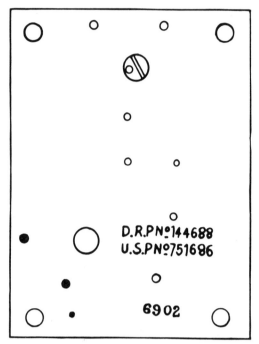

D.R.P.N°144688
U.S.P.N°751686

6902

Plate 1055 Disc Pendulum
USE .0038″ (.097mm) HOROLOVAR
(19 x 36)

EDGAR HENN

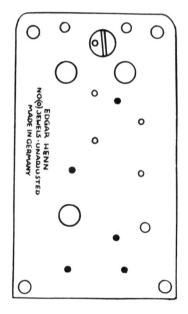

EDGAR HENN
NO(0)JEWELS · UNADJUSTED
MADE IN GERMANY

Plate 1057 4-Weight Pendulum
Miniature Clock
USE .0023″ (.058mm) HOROLOVAR
Units 29A, 29B (19 x 32)

EDGAR HENN

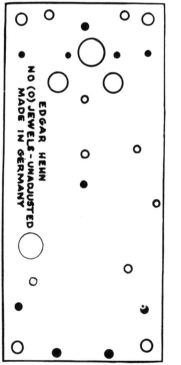

EDGAR HENN
NO (0) JEWELS - UNADJUSTED
MADE IN GERMANY

Plate Plate 1057A 4-Ball Pendulum
USE .0037″ (.094mm) HOROLOVAR
Unit 32 (19 x 38)

EHF (E. F. Henn)

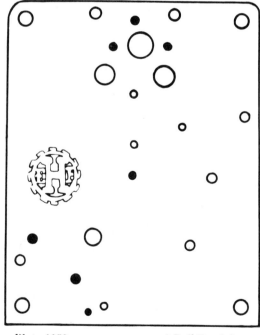

Plate 1059 4-Ball Pendulum
USE .0035″ (.089mm) HOROLOVAR
Unit 31 (19 x 38)

EHF (E. F. Henn)

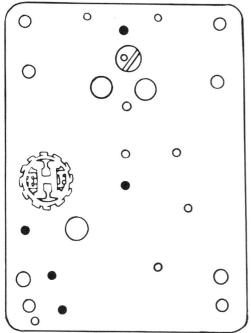

Plate 1063   4-Ball Pendulum
USE .0035″ (.089mm) HOROLOVAR
         (19 x 36)

EMO WATCH CO.

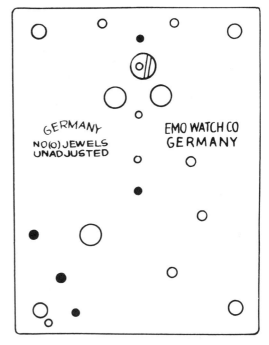

GERMANY

NO(O) JEWELS
UNADJUSTED

EMO WATCH CO
GERMANY

Plate 1067   4-Ball Pendulum
USE .004″ (.102mm) HOROLOVAR
Unit 27A   (19 x 36)

EMO WATCH CO.

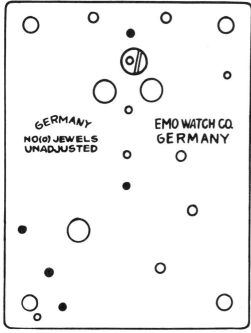

GERMANY

NO(O) JEWELS
UNADJUSTED

EMO WATCH CO.
GERMANY

Plate 1071   4-Ball Pendulum
         Hour Striker
USE .004″ (.102mm) HOROLOVAR
Unit 27A   (19 x 36)

E.R.

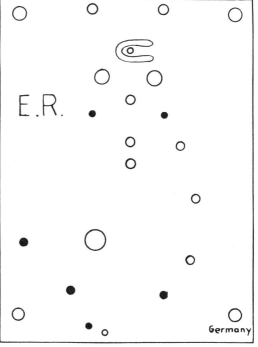

E.R.

Germany

Plate 1075   4-Ball Pendulum
USE .0032″ (.081mm) HOROLOVAR
Units 1, 3A   (19 x 38)

EULE

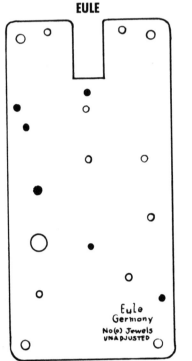

Plate 1076 4-Ball Pendulum
USE .0035″ (.089mm) HOROLOVAR
(19 x 38)

EURAMCA TRADING CO.

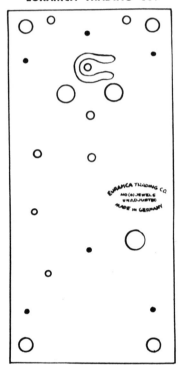

Plate 1077 4-Ball Pendulum
USE .0037″ (.094mm) HOROLOVAR
Units 16, 17 (19 x 38)

EURAMCA TRADING CORP.

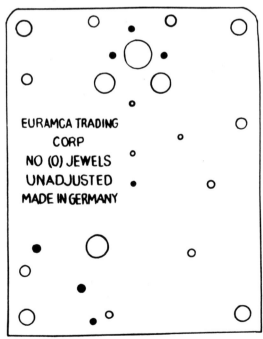

Plate 1079 4-Ball Pendulum
USE .0035″ (.089mm) HOROLOVAR
Unit 31 (19 x 38)

EURAMCA TRADING CORP.

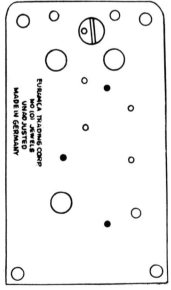

Plate 1087 4-Ball Pendulum
Miniature Clock
USE .0023″ (.058mm) HOROLOVAR
Units 29A, 29B (19 x 32)

64

EURAMCA TRADING CORP.

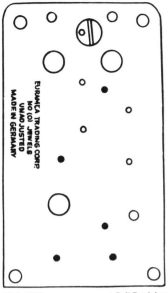

Plate 1088   4-Ball Pendulum
                                  Miniature Clock
USE .0023″ (.058mm) HOROLOVAR
Units 29A, 29B   (19 x 32)

EURAMCA TRADING CORP.

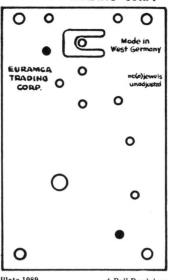

Plate 1089   4-Ball Pendulum
USE .0023″ (.058mm) HOROLOVAR
Unit 5E
USE .0022″— (.056mm—) HOROLOVAR
Unit 5F   (14 x 30)

EURAMCA TRADING CORP.

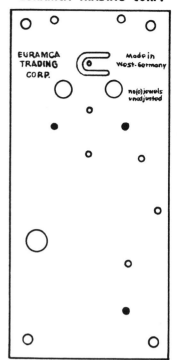

Plate 1090   4-Ball Pendulum
USE .0032″ (.081mm) HOROLOVAR
Unit 3C   (19 x 38)

EURAMCA TRADING CORP.

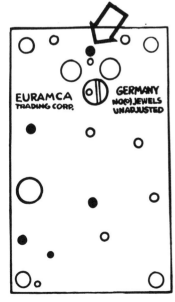

Plate 1091   Standard 4-Ball Pendulum
                          Miniature Movement
USE .003″ (.076mm) HOROLOVAR
Units 22, 23A, 24   (16 x 36)

EURAMCA TRADING CORP.

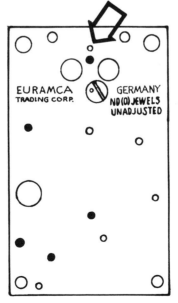

Plate 1092   Standard 4-Ball Pendulum
                          Miniature Movement
USE .0032″ (.081mm) HOROLOVAR
Unit 23B   (16 x 36)

EURAMCA TRADING CORP.

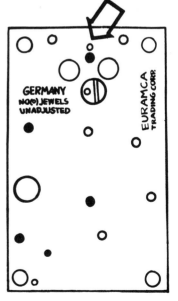

Plate 1092A   Standard 4-Ball Pendulum
                          Miniature Movement
USE .0032″ (.081mm) HOROLOVAR
Unit 23B   (16 x 36)

EURAMCA TRADING CORP.

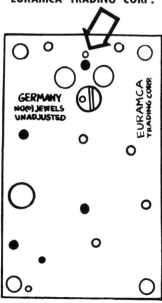

Plate 1092'B   Standard 4-Ball Pendulum
                   Miniature Movement
USE .0032" (.081mm) HOROLOVAR
Unit 23B   (16 x 36)

EURAMCA TRADING CORP.

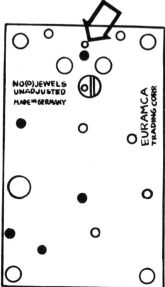

Plate 1093   4-Ball Pendulum
                         Miniature Clock
USE .0028" (.071mm) HOROLOVAR
Unit 28C   (16 x 36)

EURAMCA TRADING CORP.

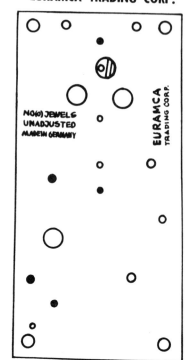

Plate 1096   4-Ball Pendulum
USE .0035" (.089mm) HOROLOVAR
Units 19, 20A, 21
USE .0038" (.097mm) HOROLOVAR
Unit 27B   (19 x 36)

EURAMCA TRADING CORP.

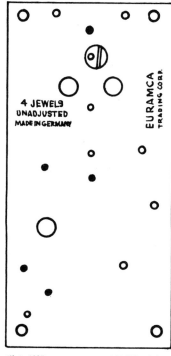

Plate 1097   4-Ball Pendulum
USE .0035" (.089mm) HOROLOVAR
Units 19, 20A, 21
USE .0038" (.097mm) HOROLOVAR
Unit 27B   (19 x 36)

EURAMCA TRADING CORP.

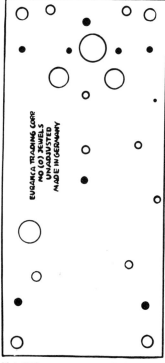

Plate 1098   4-Ball Pendulum
USE .0035" (.089mm) HOROLOVAR
Unit 31   (19 x 38)

EURAMCA TRADING CORP.

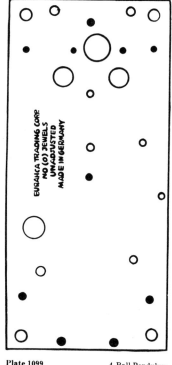

Plate 1099   4-Ball Pendulum
USE .0037" (.094mm) HOROLOVAR
Unit 32   (19 x 38)

F

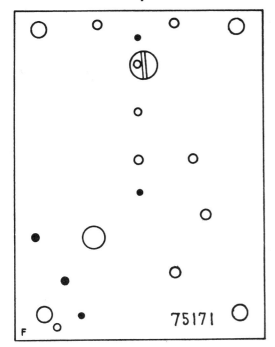

Plate 1101 Disc Pendulum
USE .004″ (.102mm) HOROLOVAR
(19 x 36)

FHS (F. S. Hermle)

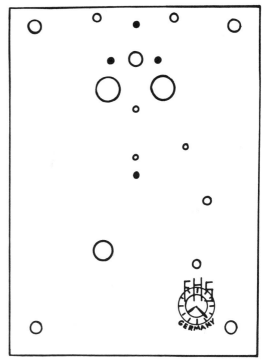

Plate 1103 4-Ball Pendulum
USE .0033″ (.084mm) HOROLOVAR
Unit 25A (18 x 38)

FHS (F. S. Hermle)

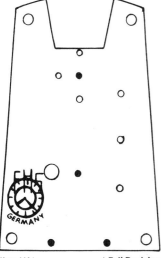

Plate 1104 4-Ball Pendulum
Miniature Clock
USE .0022″ (.056mm) HOROLOVAR
Unit 25B (13 x 30)

FORESTVILLE

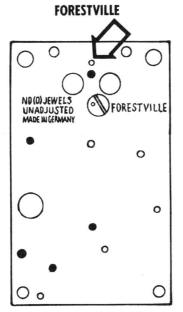

NO(0) JEWELS
UNADJUSTED
MADE IN GERMANY

FORESTVILLE

Plate 1105 Miniature Movement
Standard 4-Ball Pendulum
Use .0032″ (.081mm) HOROLOVAR
Unit 23B (16 x 36)

FORESTVILLE

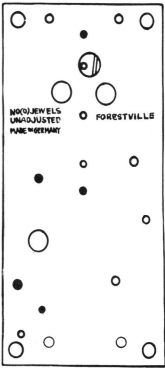

NO(0) JEWELS
UNADJUSTED
MADE IN GERMANY

FORESTVILLE

Plate 1105A 4-Ball Pendulum
USE .0035″ (.089mm) HOROLOVAR
Units 19, 20A, 21
USE .0038″ (.097mm) HOROLOVAR
Unit 27B (19 x 36)

FORESTVILLE CLOCK CO.

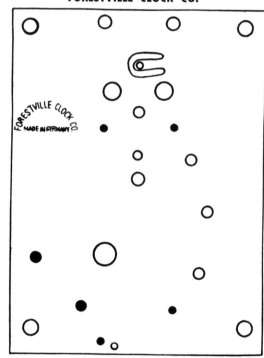

NO(0)JEWELS
UNADJUSTED
MADE IN GERMANY

FORESTVILLE
CLOCK CO. INC.

Plate 1106　　　Standard 4-Ball Pendulum
Miniature Movement
USE .003″ (.076mm) HOROLOVAR
Units 22, 23A, 24　　　　　　　(16 x 36)

FORESTVILLE CLOCK CO.

FORESTVILLE CLOCK CO
MADE IN GERMANY

Plate 1107　　　　　　4-Ball Pendulum
USE .0032″ (.081mm) HOROLOVAR
Units 1, 3A　　　　　　　　(19 x 38)

FORESTVILLE CLOCK CO.

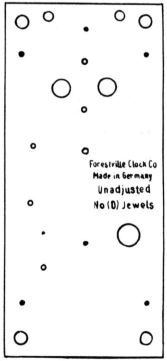

Forestville Clock Co
Made in Germany
Unadjusted
No (0) Jewels

Plate 1111　　　　　4-Ball Pendulum
USE .0037″ (.094mm) HOROLOVAR
Units 16, 17　　　　　　　(19 x 38)

FORESTVILLE CLOCK CO.

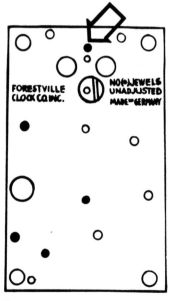

FORESTVILLE
CLOCK CO. INC.

NO(0)JEWELS
UNADJUSTED
MADE IN GERMANY

Plate 1115　　　　Miniature Movement
Standard 4-Ball Pendulum
USE .003″ (.076mm) HOROLOVAR
Units 22, 23A, 24　　　　　(16 x 36)

FORESTVILLE CLOCK CO.

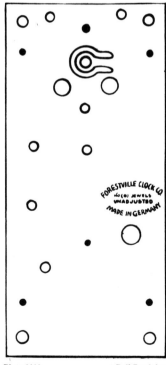

FORESTVILLE CLOCK CO
NO (0) JEWELS
UNADJUSTED
MADE IN GERMANY

Plate 1119　　　　　4-Ball Pendulum
USE .0037″ (.094mm) HOROLOVAR
Units 16, 17　　　　　　　(19 x 38)

FRANZ HERMLE

Plate 1124

4-Ball Pendulum
Miniature Clock

USE .0022″ (.056mm) HOROLOVAR
Unit 25B   (13 x 30)

FRANZ HERMLE

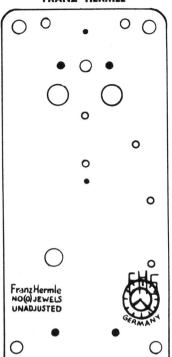

Plate 1126   4-Ball Pendulum
USE .0033″ (.084mm) HOROLOVAR
Unit 25A   (18 x 38)

FRED J. KOCH

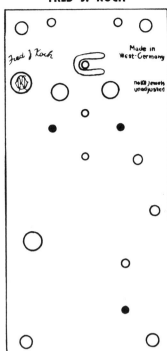

Plate 1135   4-Ball Pendulum
USE .0032″ (.081mm) HOROLOVAR
Units 1, 3A, 3B, 3C   (19 x 38)

FRED J. KOCH

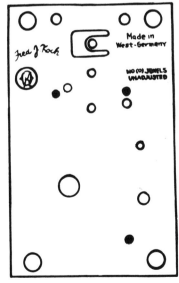

Plate 1139   4-Ball Pendulum
                                  Miniature Clock
USE .0023″ (.058mm) HOROLOVAR
Units 5A, 5B, 5C, 5D, 5E   (14 x 30)

FRED J. KOCH

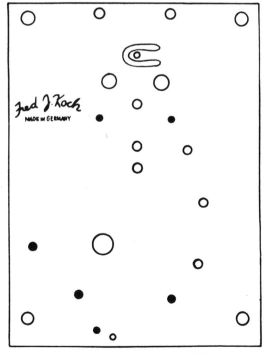

Plate 1143   4-Ball Pendulum
USE .0032″ (.081mm) HOROLOVAR
Units 1, 3A   (19 x 38)

FR. VOSSELER

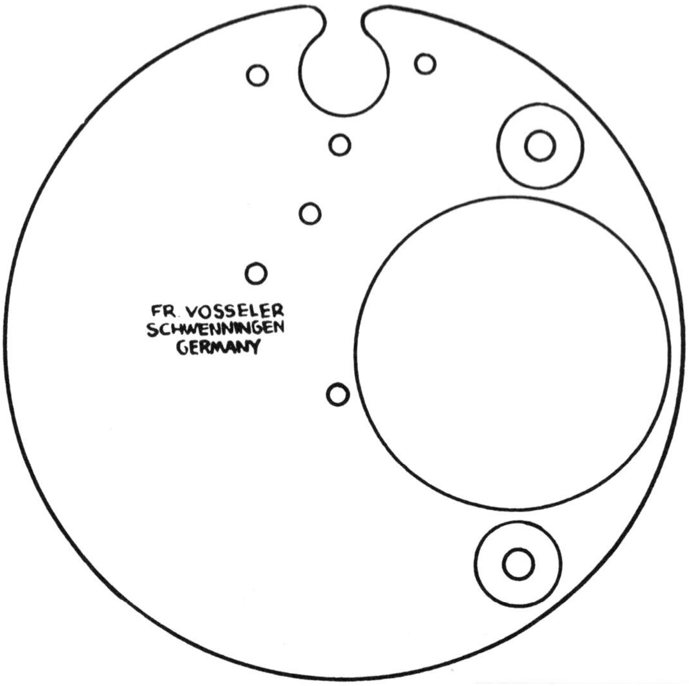

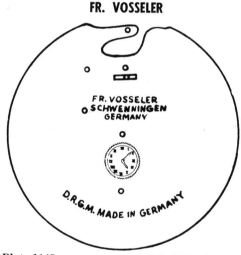

FR. VOSSELER
SCHWENNINGEN
GERMANY

Plate 1144 4-Ball Pendulum
Underslung Suspension
USE .0028″ (.071mm) HOROLOVAR
(19 x 36)

FR. VOSSELER

FR. VOSSELER
SCHWENNINGEN
GERMANY

D.R.G.M. MADE IN GERMANY

Plate 1145 3-Ball Pendulum
Miniature "Louvre" Clock
Underslung Suspension
USE .0035″* (.089mm*) HOROLOVAR

G

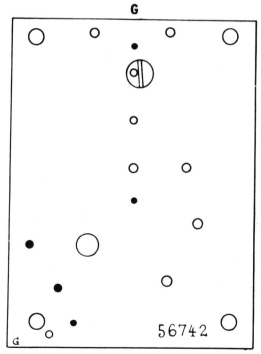

56742

Plate 1146 Disc Pendulum
7³⁄₁₆″ Suspension Spring
USE .005″− (.127mm−) HOROLOVAR
(19 x 36)

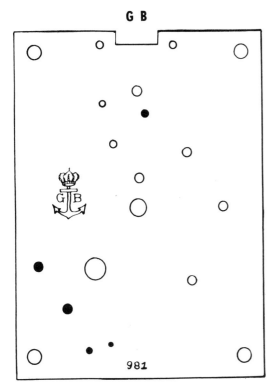

G B

981

Plate 1147   4-Ball Pendulum
Pin Pallet Escapement
Lantern Pinions
USE .004″ (.102mm) HOROLOVAR
(19 x 38)

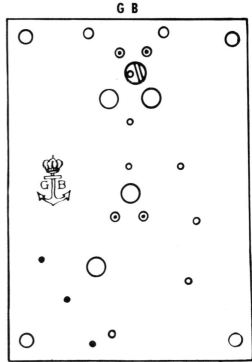

G B

Plate 1149   Disc Pendulum
4-Ball Pendulum
Overhead Suspension
USE .004″ (.102mm) HOROLOVAR
(19 x 38)

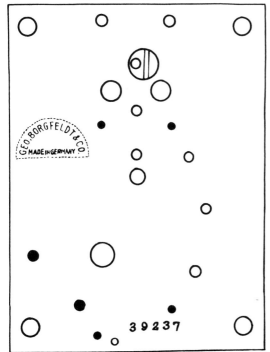

GEO. BORGFELDT & CO.

39237

Plate 1151   4-Ball Pendulum
USE .0032″ (.081mm) HOROLOVAR
Units 1, 3A   (19 x 38)

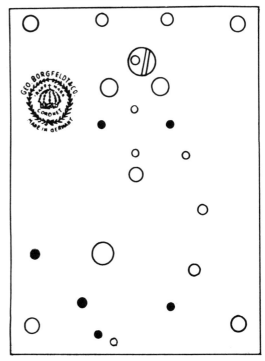

GEO. BORGFELDT & CO.

Plate 1155   4-Ball Pendulum
USE .0032″ (.081mm) HOROLOVAR
Units 1, 3A   (19 x 38)

GEORG WURTHNER

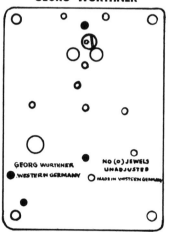

GEORG WURTHNER
.WESTERN GERMANY

NO (0) JEWELS
UNADJUSTED
MADE IN WESTERN GERMANY

Plate 1157   4-Ball Pendulum
                                  Midget Clock
USE .002″ (.051mm) HOROLOVAR
Unit 37   (9.5 x 27)

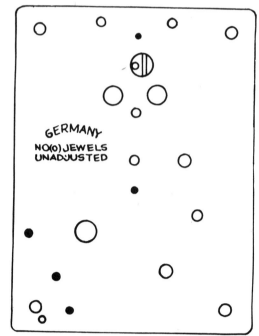

GERMANY
NO(0)JEWELS
UNADJUSTED

Plate 1159   4-Ball Pendulum
USE .004″ (.102mm) HOROLOVAR
Unit 27A   (19 x 36)

GERMANY

NO(0)JEWELS
UNADJUSTED
GERMANY

Plate 1161   4-Ball Pendulum
                                  Midget Clock
USE .0019″ (.048mm) HOROLOVAR
Unit 39   (12 x 25)

GERMANY

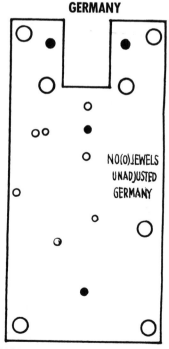

NO(0)JEWELS
UNADJUSTED
GERMANY

Plate 1162   4-Ball Pendulum
USE .0035″ (.089mm) HOROLOVAR
                                    (18 x 38)

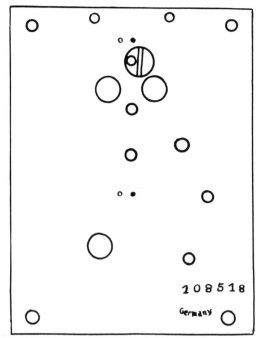

GERMANY

Plate 1163   Disc Pendulum
USE .0035″* (.089mm*) HOROLOVAR
                              (18 x 38)

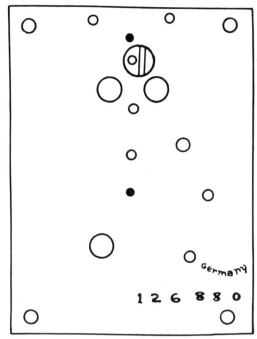

GERMANY

Plate 1167   Disc Pendulum
USE .0035″* (.089mm*) HOROLOVAR
                              (18 x 38)

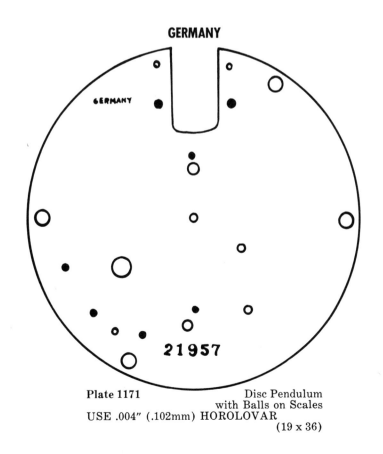

GERMANY

Plate 1171   Disc Pendulum
                    with Balls on Scales
USE .004″ (.102mm) HOROLOVAR
                             (19 x 36)

73

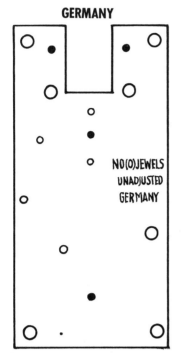

GERMANY

NO (0) JEWELS
UNADJUSTED
GERMANY

Plate 1173   4-Ball Pendulum
USE .0035″ (.089mm) HOROLOVAR
(18 x 38)

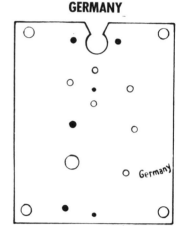

GERMANY

Germany

Plate 1175   Semispherical Pendulum
Miniature Clock: 5″ High
Pin Pallet Escapement
USE .002″— (.051mm—) HOROLOVAR

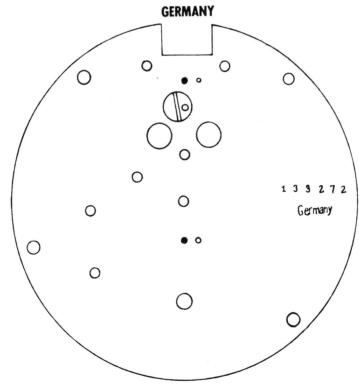

GERMANY

1 3 3 2 7 2
Germany

Plate 1183   Disc Pendulum
Front Wind
USE .0035″ (.089mm) HOROLOVAR
(19 x 38)

74

GERMANY

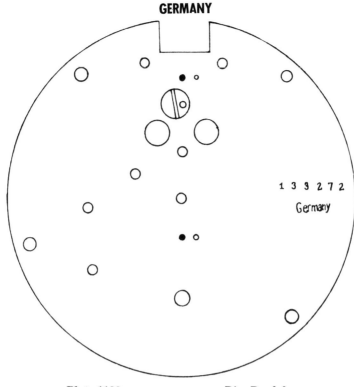

1 3 3 2 7 2
Germany

Plate 1183   Disc Pendulum
                                      Front Wind
USE .0035″ (.089mm) HOROLOVAR
                                    (19 x 38)

GUSTAV BECKER

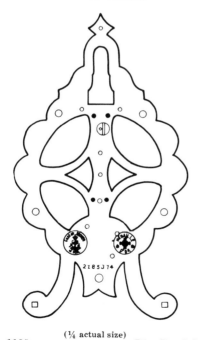

(¼ actual size)

Plate 1189   Disc Pendulum
                                    Skeleton Clock
USE .004″ (.102mm) HOROLOVAR
                                    (19 x 38)

GUSTAV BECKER

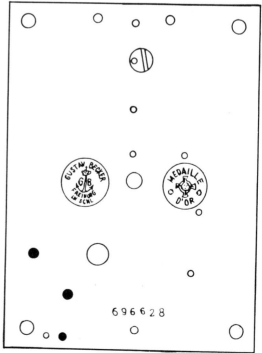

6 9 6 6 2 8

Plate 1191   Disc Pendulum
                                  4-Ball Pendulum
USE .004″ (.102mm) HOROLOVAR
                                    (19 x 38)

GUSTAV BECKER

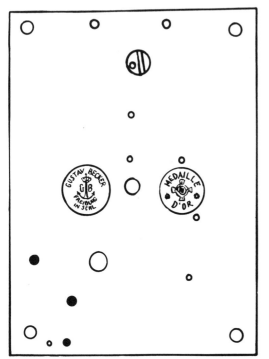

Plate 1195   Disc Pendulum
                                  4-Ball Pendulum
USE .004″ (.102mm) HOROLOVAR
                                  (19 x 38)

GUSTAV BECKER

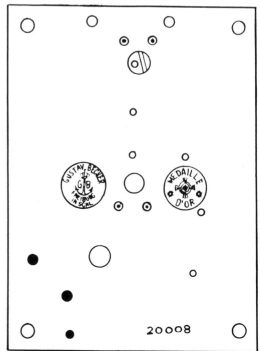

20008

Plate 1199   Disc Pendulum
                                  4-Ball Pendulum
USE .004″ (.102mm) HOROLOVAR
                                  (19 x 38)

GUSTAV BECKER

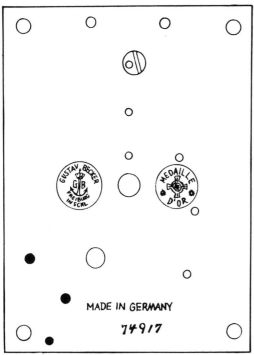

MADE IN GERMANY

74917

Plate 1203   Disc Pendulum
                                  4-Ball Pendulum
USE .004″ (.102mm) HOROLOVAR
                                  (19 x 38)

GUSTAV BECKER

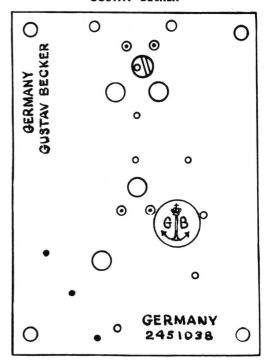

GERMANY
2451038

Plate 1206   Disc Pendulum
USE .004″ (.102mm) HOROLOVAR
                                  (19 x 38)

76

GUSTAV BECKER

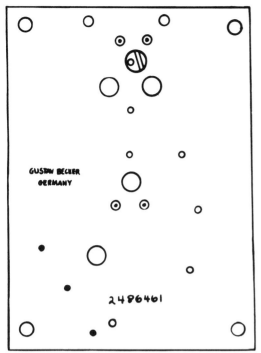

Plate 1207   Disc Pendulum
                                  4-Ball Pendulum
USE .004″ (.102mm) HOROLOVAR
                                      (19 x 38)

GUSTAV BECKER

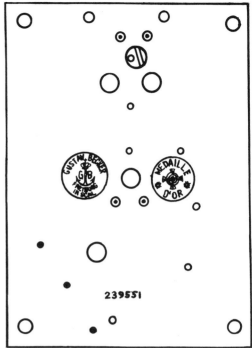

Plate 1207A   Disc Pendulum
                                    4-Ball Pendulum
USE .004″ (.102mm) HOROLOVAR
                                      (19 x 38)

GUTENBACHER UHRENFABRIK

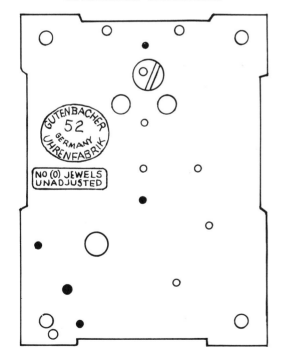

Plate 1208   4-Ball Pendulum
USE .004″ (.102mm) HOROLOVAR
Unit 27A   (19 x 36)

HALL CRAFT CORP.

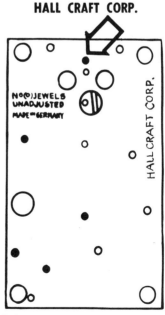

Plate 1209   4-Ball Pendulum
                                  Miniature Clock
USE .0025″ (.064mm) HOROLOVAR
Units 28A, 28B   (16 x 36)

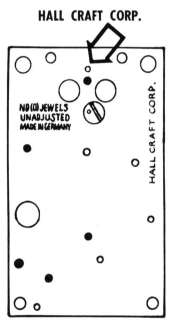

Plate 1210   4-Ball Pendulum
                                    Miniature Clock
USE .0028″ (.071mm) HOROLOVAR
Unit 28C   (16 x 36)

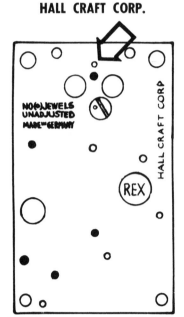

Plate 1210A   4-Ball Pendulum
                                    Miniature Clock
USE .0028″ (.071mm) HOROLOVAR
Unit 28C   (16 x 36)

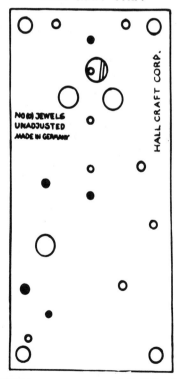

Plate 1211A   4-Ball Pendulum
USE .0035″ (.089mm) HOROLOVAR
Units 19, 20A, 21
USE .0038″ (.097mm) HOROLOVAR
Unit 27B   (19 x 36)

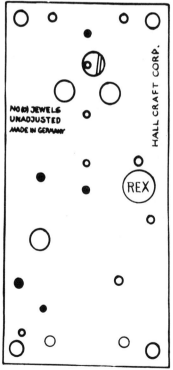

Plate 1212   4-Ball Pendulum
USE .0035″ (.089mm) HOROLOVAR
Units 19, 20A, 21
USE .0038″ (.097mm) HOROLOVAR
Unit 27B   (19 x 36)

HASI

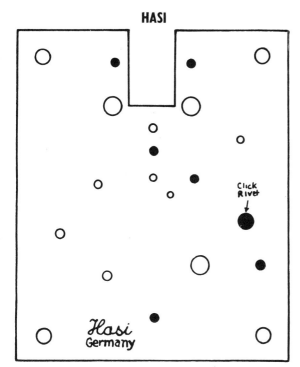

Click Rivet

Hasi
Germany

Plate 1213   4-Ball Pendulum
USE .003″ (.076mm) HOROLOVAR
            (18 x 38)

HASI·

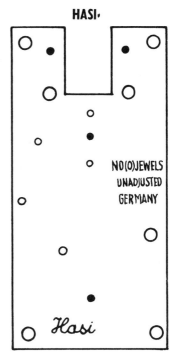

NO(O)JEWELS
UNADJUSTED
GERMANY

Hasi

Plate 1213A   4-Ball Pendulum
USE .0035″ (.089mm) HOROLOVAR
            (18 x 38)

H. COEHLER CO.

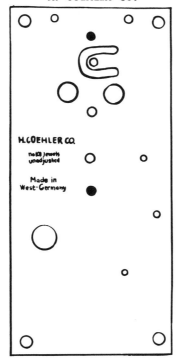

H.COEHLER CO.

no(0) Jewels
unadjusted

Made in
West-Germany

Plate 1214   4-Ball Pendulum
USE .004″ (.102mm) HOROLOVAR
Units 6, 7, 8, 9   (19 x 38)

H. COEHLER CO. INC.

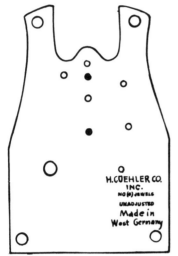

Plate 1214A

Dome Clock—3-Ball Pendulum
Coach Clock—4-Ball Pendulum
USE .0023″ (.058mm) HOROLOVAR
Unit 10A   (13 x 30)

H. COEHLER CO. INC.

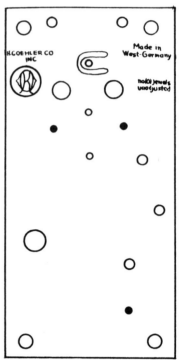

Plate 1214C   4-Ball Pendulum
USE .0032″ (.081mm) HOROLOVAR
Units 1, 3A, 3B, 3C   (19 x 38)

HECO

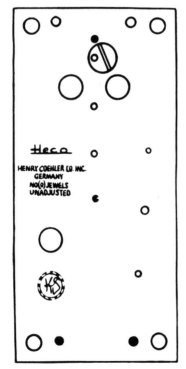

Plate 1216   4-Ball Pendulum
USE .0036″ (.091mm) HOROLOVAR
Unit 11B   (18 x 38)

HECO

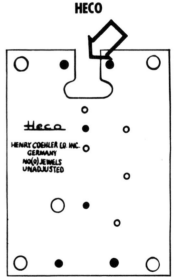

Plate 1217   4-Ball Pendulum
                                  Miniature Clock
USE .002″ (.051mm) HOROLOVAR
Units 12A, 12B, 12C
USE .0019″ (.048mm) HOROLOVAR
Unit 12D   (12 x 25)

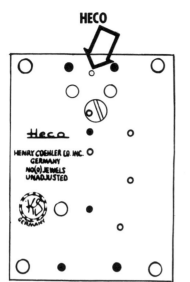

Plate 1217A   4-Ball Pendulum
                              Miniature Clock
USE .002″ (.051mm) HOROLOVAR
Units 12A, 12B, 12C
USE .0019″ (.048mm) HOROLOVAR
Unit 12D   (12 x 25)

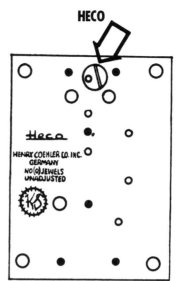

Plate 1217B   4-Ball Pendulum
                              Miniature Clock
USE .002″ (.051mm) HOROLOVAR
Units 12A, 12B, 12C
USE .0019″ (.048mm) HOROLOVAR
Unit 12D   (12 x 25)

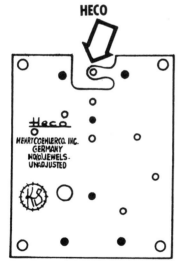

Plate 1217C   4-Ball or Disc Pendulum
                              Midget Clock
                        Pin Pallet Escapement
USE .002″ (.051mm) HOROLOVAR
Unit 12E   (14 x 25)

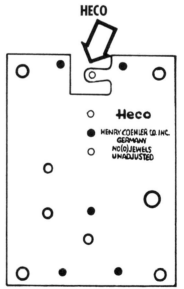

Plate 1217F   4-Ball Pendulum
                              Miniature Clock
USE .0023″ (.058mm) HOROLOVAR
Unit 12F   (14 x 30)

HECO

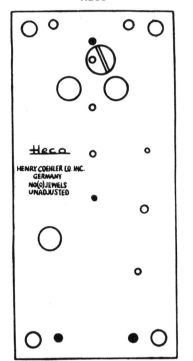

Plate 1218   4-Ball Pendulum
USE .0036″ (.091mm) HOROLOVAR
Unit 11B   (18 x 38)

H. EICKMANN & CO.

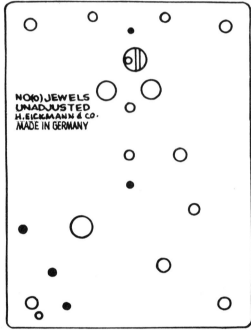

Plate 1221   4-Ball Pendulum
USE .004″ (.102mm) HOROLOVAR
Unit 27A   (19 x 36)

HENRY COEHLER

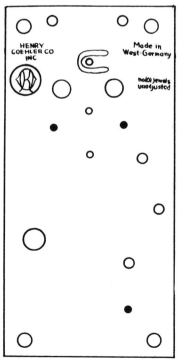

Plate 1222   4-Ball Pendulum
     Miniature Clock
USE .0025″ (.064mm) HOROLOVAR
Units 28A, 28B   (16 x 36)

HENRY COEHLER CO. INC.

Plate 1227   4-Ball Pendulum
USE .0032″ (.081mm) HOROLOVAR
Units 1, 3A, 3B, 3C   (19 x 38)

HENRY COEHLER CO. INC.

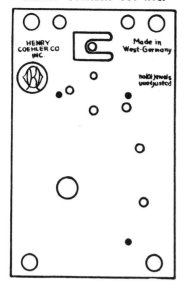

Plate 1231
USE .0023" (.058mm) HOROLOVAR
Units 5A, 5B, 5C, 5D, 5E

4-Ball Pendulum
Miniature Clock

(14 x 30)

HENRY COEHLER CO. INC.

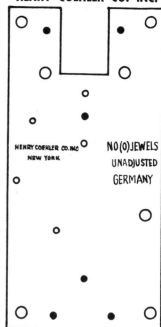

Plate 1232
USE .0035" (.089mm) HOROLOVAR

4-Ball Pendulum

(18 x 38)

HENRY COEHLER CO. INC.

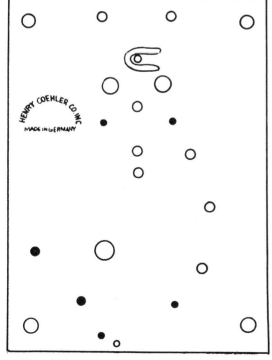

Plate 1239
USE .0032" (.081mm) HOROLOVAR
Units 1, 3A

4-Ball Pendulum

(19 x 38)

HERR

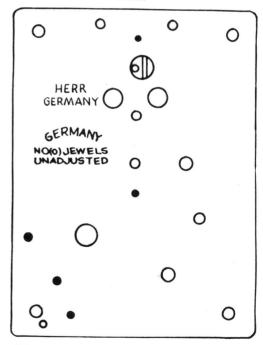

Plate 1241
USE .004" (.102mm) HOROLOVAR
Unit 27A

4-Ball Pendulum

(19 x 36)

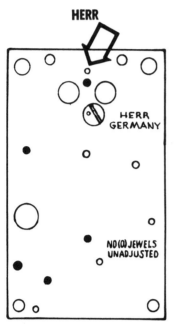

Plate 1243　　　　　4-Ball Pendulum
　　　　　　　　　　　　Miniature Clock
USE .0025″ (.064mm) HOROLOVAR
Units 28A, 28B　　　　　　　(16 x 36)

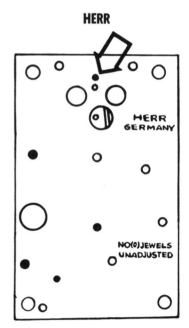

Plate 1244　　　　　4-Ball Pendulum
　　　　　　　　　　　　Miniature Clock
USE .0028″ (.071mm) HOROLOVAR
Unit 28C　　　　　　　　　(16 x 36)

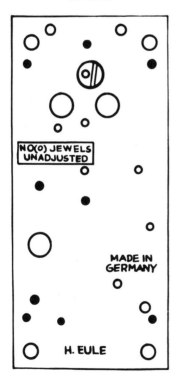

Plate 1245　　　　　4-Ball Pendulum
USE .004″ (.102mm) HOROLOVAR
Unit 26　　　　　　　　　(19 x 36)

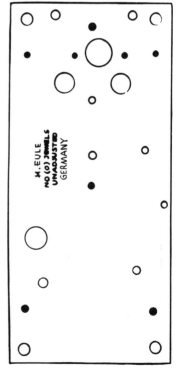

Plate 1246　　　　　4-Ball Pendulum
USE .0037″ (.094mm) HOROLOVAR
Unit 32　　　　　　　　　(19 x 38)

H. EULE

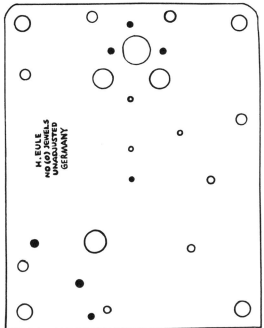

Plate 1246A   4-Ball Pendulum
USE .0035″ (.089mm) HOROLOVAR
Unit 31   (19 x 38)

HUBER UHREN

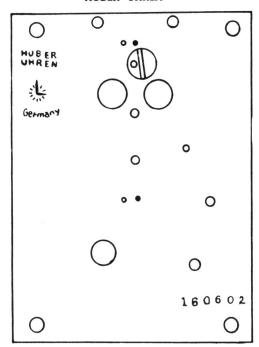

Plate 1247   4-Ball Pendulum
USE .0035″ (.089mm) HOROLOVAR
                     (19 x 38)

HUBER UHREN

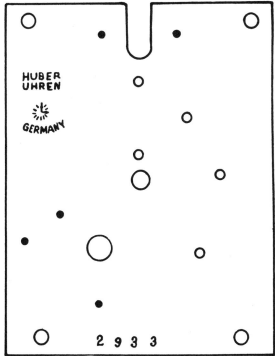

Plate 1251   Disc Pendulum
          Pin Pallet Escapement
              Lantern Pinions
USE .0037″ (.094mm) HOROLOVAR
                   (20 x 38)

H.X.M.

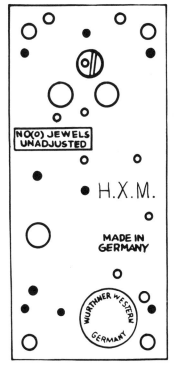

Plate 1252   4-Ball Pendulum
USE .004″ (.102mm) HOROLOVAR
Unit 26   (19 x 36)

H.Z.

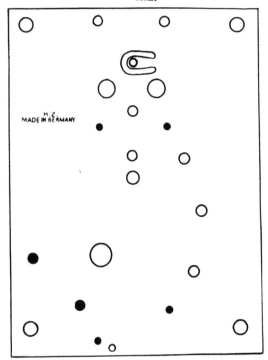

Plate 1253   4-Ball Pendulum
USE .0032″ (.081mm) HOROLOVAR
Units 1, 3A   (19 x 38)

HZ

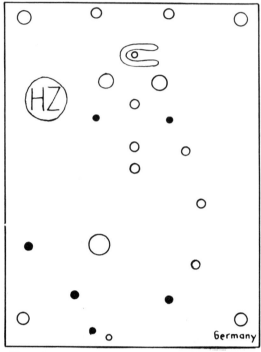

Plate 1254   4-Ball Pendulum
USE .0032″ (.081mm) HOROLOVAR
Units 1, 3A   (19 x 38)

JAHRESUHREN-FABRIK

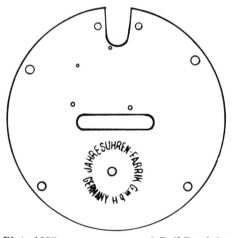

Plate 1257   3-Ball Pendulum
USE .0032″* (.081mm*) HOROLOVAR

JAHRESUHREN-FABRIK

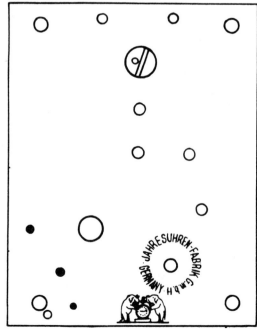

Plate 1259   4-Ball Pendulum
USE .004″ (.102mm) HOROLOVAR
Units 6, 7, 8, 9   (19 x 36)

JAHRESUHREN-FABRIK

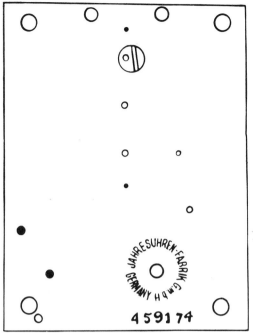

Plate 1263   4-Ball Pendulum
USE .004″ (.102mm) HOROLOVAR·
Units 6, 7, 8, 9   (19 x 36)

JAHRESUHREN-FABRIK

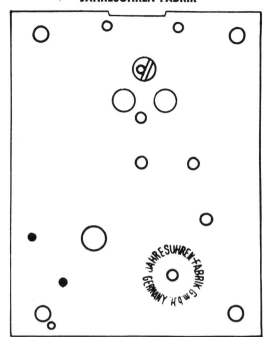

Plate 1265   4-Ball Pendulum
USE .004″ (.102mm) HOROLOVAR
Units 6, 7, 8, 9   (19 x 36)

JAHRESUHREN-FABRIK

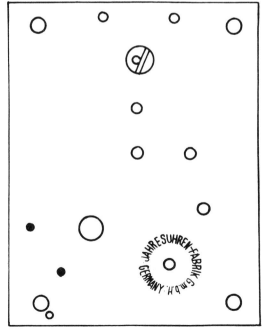

Plate 1267   4-Ball Pendulum
USE .004″ (.102mm) HOROLOVAR
Units 6, 7, 8, 9   (19 x 36)

JAHRESUHRENFABRIK

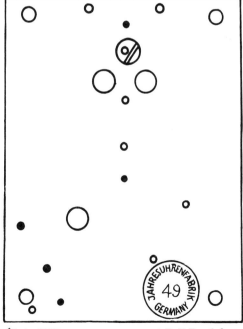

Plate 1271   4-Ball Pendulum
USE .004″ (.102mm) HOROLOVAR
Units 6, 7, 8, 9   (19 x 36)

JAHRESUHRENFABRIK

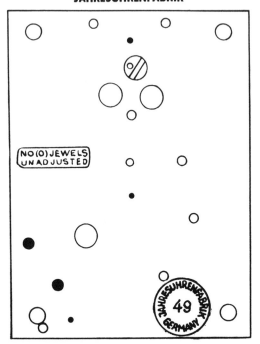

Plate 1278   4-Ball Pendulum
USE .004″ (.102mm) HOROLOVAR
Units 6, 7, 8, 9   (19 x 36)

JAHRESUHRENFABRIK

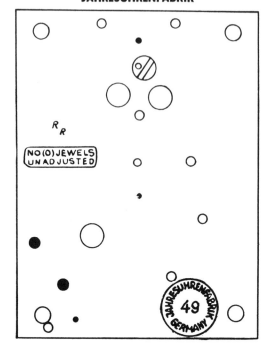

Plate 1279   4-Ball Pendulum
USE .004″ (.102mm) HOROLOVAR
Units 6, 7, 8, 9   (19 x 36)

JAHRESUHRENFABRIK

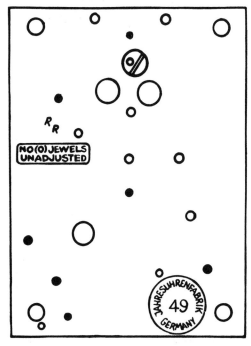

Plate 1283   4-Ball Pendulum
USE .004″ (.102mm) HOROLOVAR
Units 6, 7, 8, 9   (19 x 36)

JAHRESUHRENFABRIK

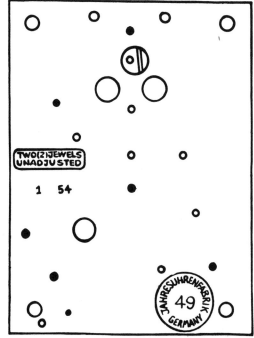

Plate 1287   4-Ball Pendulum
USE .004″ (.102mm) HOROLOVAR
Units 6, 7, 8, 9   (19 x 36)

JAHRESUHRENFABRIK

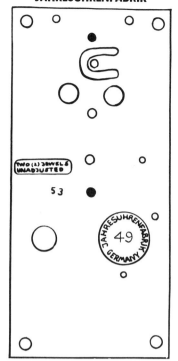

Plate 1291   4-Ball Pendulum
USE .004″ (.102mm) HOROLOVAR
Units 6, 7, 8, 9   (19 x 36)

JAHRESUHRENFABRIK

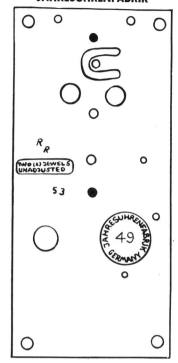

Plate 1291A   4-Ball Pendulum
USE .004″ (.102mm) HOROLOVAR
Units 6, 7, 8, 9   (19 x 36)

JAHRESUHRENFABRIK

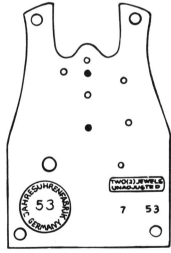

Plate 1299
      Dome Clock—3-Ball Pendulum
      Coach Clock—4-Ball Pendulum
USE .0023″ (.058mm) HOROLOVAR
Unit 10 A   (13 x 30)

JAHRESUHR SYLVESTER

      (½ actual size)
Plate 1303   3″ Ball Pendulum
Duplex Escapement
Hour and Half Hour Gong Strike
11″ Suspension Spring
USE .006″– (.152mm–) HOROLOVAR

      (½ actual size)
Plate 1307   3″ Ball Pendulum
Duplex Escapement
Hour and Half Hour Bell Strike
4½″ Suspension Spring
USE .0036″ (.091mm) HOROLOVAR

J H

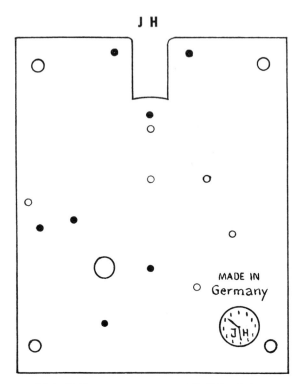

Plate 1308   4-Ball Pendulum
USE .0038″ (.097mm) HOROLOVAR
Unit 33   (19 x 38)

J. KAISER G.M.B.H.

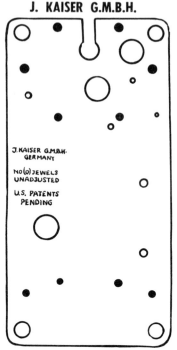

Plate 1309   Ball Pendulum
USE .003″ (.076mm) HOROLOVAR
Unit 34   (19 x 38)

J. KAISER G.M.B.H.

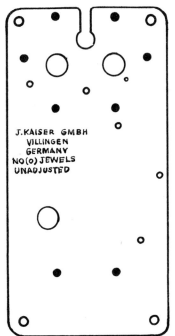

Plate 1309A   Ball Pendulum
USE .003″ (.076mm) HOROLOVAR
Unit 34   (19 x 38)

J. KAISER G.M.B.H.

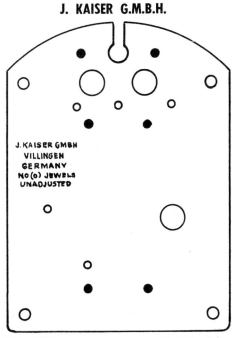

Plate 1310   Ball Pendulum
USE .003″ (.076mm) HOROLOVAR
Unit 34   (19 x 38)

J. KAISER G.M.B.H.

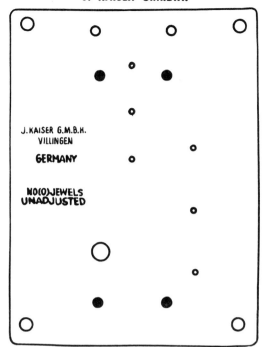

J. KAISER G.M.B.H.
VILLINGEN

GERMANY

NO(0) JEWELS
UNADJUSTED

Plate 1312 4-Ball Pendulum
USE .0033″ (.084mm) HOROLOVAR
Unit 18B, 18C (19 x 38)

J K G

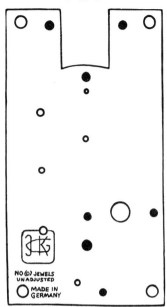

NO (0) JEWELS
UNADJUSTED

MADE IN
GERMANY

Plate 1313 ·4-Ball Pendulum
Miniature Movement
USE .0032″ (.081mm) HOROLOVAR
Unit 14 (13 x 32)

J. LINK & CO.

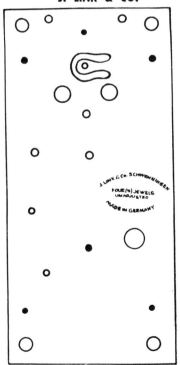

J. LINK & Co. SCHWENNINGEN

FOUR (4) JEWELS
UNADJUSTED

MADE IN GERMANY

Plate 1314 4-Ball Pendulum
USE .0037″ (.094mm) HOROLOVAR
Units 16, 17 (19 x 38)

J. LINK & CO.

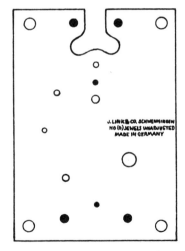

J. LINK & CO. SCHWENNINGEN
NO (0) JEWELS UNADJUSTED
MADE IN GERMANY

Plate 1316 4-Ball Pendulum
Miniature Clock
USE .0021″ (.053mm) HOROLOVAR
Unit 35 (14 x 28)

J. MULLER & CO.

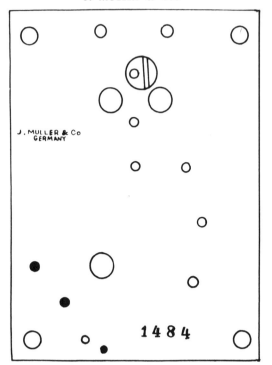

Plate 1317   4-Ball Pendulum
USE .0035″* (.089mm*) HOROLOVAR
                    (19 x 38)

J. MULLER & CO.

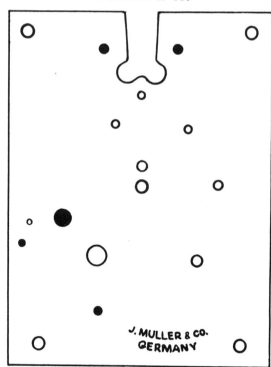

Plate 1318   3-Ball Pendulum
              Pin Pallet Escapement
                  Lantern Pinions
USE .0035″ (.089mm) HOROLOVAR (20 x 38)

JOHN WANAMAKER

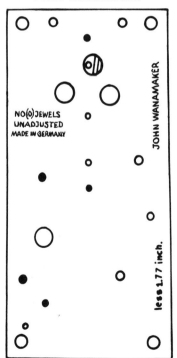

Plate 1319   4-Ball Pendulum
USE .0035″ (.089mm) HOROLOVAR
Units 19, 20A, 21   (19 x 36)

JOHN WANAMAKER

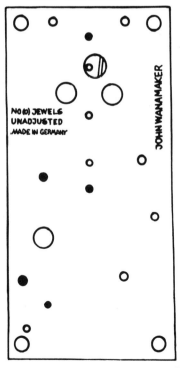

Plate 1323   4-Ball Pendulum
Dome Clock
USE .0035″ (.089mm) HOROLOVAR
Units 19, 20A, 21
Square Clock
USE .0033″ (.084mm) HOROLOVAR
Unit 20B   (19 x 36)

JOHN WANAMAKER

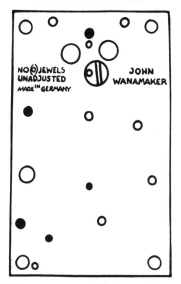

Plate 1325   Miniature Movement
Standard 4-Ball Pendulum
USE .003″ (.076mm) HOROLOVAR
Units 22, 23A, 24   (16 x 36)

JOHN WANAMAKER

Plate 1326   Standard 4-Ball Pendulum
Miniature Movement
USE .003″ (.076mm) HOROLOVAR
Units 22, 23A, 24   (16 x 36)

JOSEF F. SCOTT CO.

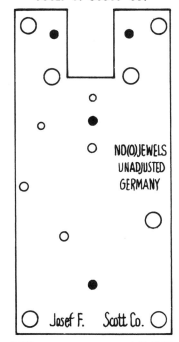

Plate 1332   4-Ball Pendulum
USE .0035″ (.089mm) HOROLOVAR
       (18 x 38)

JOSEPH HORNE CO.

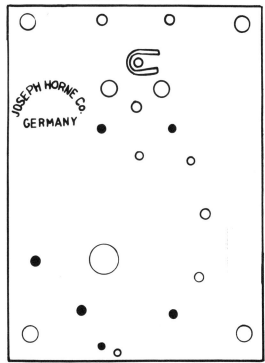

Plate 1338   4-Ball Pendulum
USE .0032″ (.081mm) HOROLOVAR
Units 1, 3A   (19 x 38)

JOSEPH KAROL

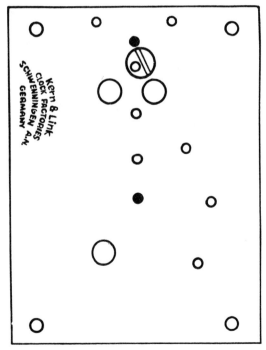

JOSEPH KAROL
TOLEDO
MADE IN GERMANY

NO(o)JEWELS
UNADJUSTED

Plate 1340   4-Ball Pendulum
USE .0035″ (.089mm) HOROLOVAR
Units 13A, 13B   (20 x 38)

KERN & LINK

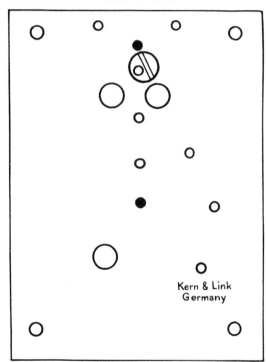

Kern & Link
Germany

Plate 1341   4-Ball Pendulum
USE .0036″ (.091mm) HOROLOVAR
Unit 11A   (18 x 38)

KERN & LINK

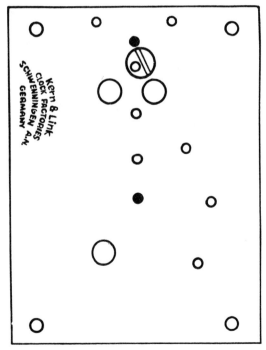

Kern & Link
CLOCK FACTORIES
SCHWENNINGEN A.N.
GERMANY

Plate 1342   4-Ball Pendulum
USE .0036″ (.091mm) HOROLOVAR
Unit 11A   (18 x 38)

KERN & SOHNE

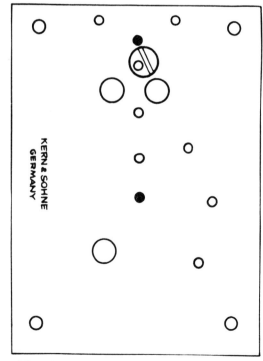

KERN & SOHNE
GERMANY

Plate 1343   4-Ball Pendulum
USE .0036″ (.091mm) HOROLOVAR
Unit 11A   (18 x 38)

KERN & SOHNE

KERN & SOHNE
GERMANY
(0) JEWELS
UNADJUSTED

Plate 1348

4-Ball Pendulum
Miniature Clock

USE .002″ (.051mm) HOROLOVAR
Units 12A, 12B, 12C   (12 x 25)

KIENINGER & OBERGFELL

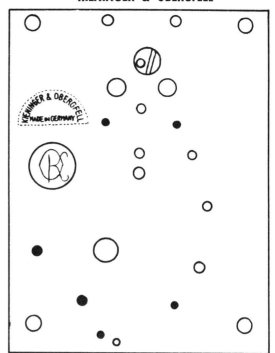

KIENINGER & OBERGFELL
MADE IN GERMANY

Plate 1351   4-Ball Pendulum
USE .0032″ (.081mm) HOROLOVAR
Units 1, 3A   (19 x 38)

KIENINGER & OBERGFELL

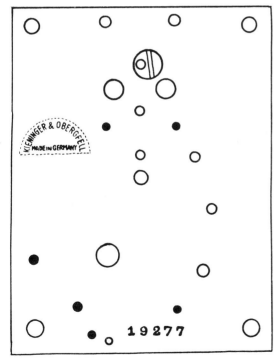

KIENINGER & OBERGFELL
MADE IN GERMANY

19277

Plate 1355   4-Ball Pendulum
USE .0032″ (.081mm) HOROLOVAR
Units 1, 3A   (19 x 38)

KIENINGER & OBERGFELL

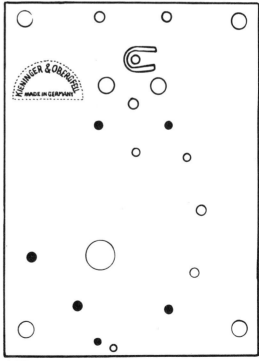

KIENINGER & OBERGFELL
MADE IN GERMANY

Plate 1359   4-Ball Pendulum
USE .0032″ (.081mm) HOROLOVAR
Units 1, 3A   (19 x 38)

KIENINGER & OBERGFELL

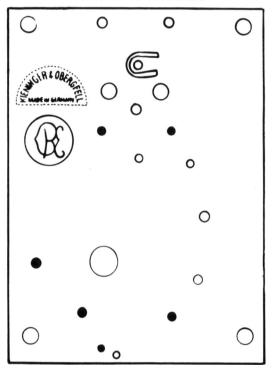

Plate 1363   4-Ball Pendulum
USE .0032″ (.081mm) HOROLOVAR
Units 1, 3A   (19 x 38)

KIENINGER & OBERGFELL

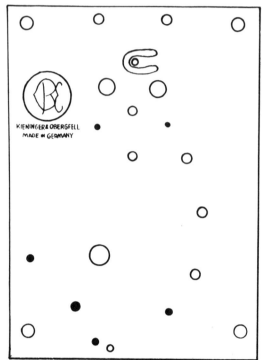

Plate 1367   4-Ball Pendulum
USE .0032″ (.081mm) HOROLOVAR
Units 1, 3A   (19 x 38)

KIENINGER & OBERGFELL

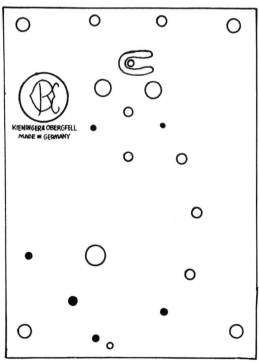

Plate 1369   4-Ball Pendulum
USE .0032″ (.081mm) HOROLOVAR
Units 1, 3A, 3B, 3C   (19 x 38)

KIENINGER & OBERGFELL

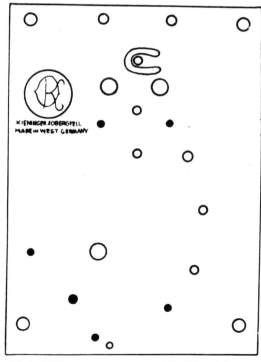

Plate 1371   4-Ball Pendulum
USE .0032″ (.081mm) HOROLOVAR
Units 1, 3A, 3B, 3C   (19 x 38)

KIENINGER & OBERGFELL

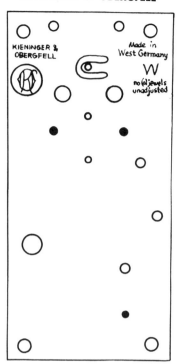

Plate 1375   4-Ball Pendulum
USE .0032″ (.081mm) HOROLOVAR
Units 1, 3A, 3B, 3C   (19 x 38)

KIENINGER & OBERGFELL

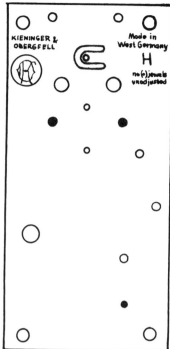

Plate 1376   4-Ball Pendulum
USE .0032″ (.081mm) HOROLOVAR
Units 1, 3A, 3B, 3C   (19 x 38)

KIENINGER & OBERGFELL

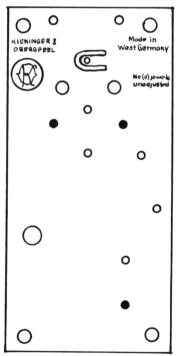

Plate 1377   4-Ball Pendulum
USE .0032″ (.081mm) HOROLOVAR
Units 1, 3A, 3B, 3C   (19 x 38)

KIENINGER & OBERGFELL

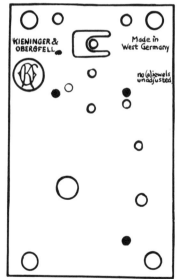

Plate 1379   4-Ball Pendulum
             Miniature Clock
USE .0023″ (.058mm) HOROLOVAR
Units 5A, 5B, 5C, 5D, 5E   (14 x 30)

KIENZLE CLOCK FACTORIES

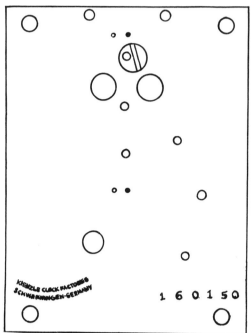

Plate 1383
USE .0036″ (.091mm) HOROLOVAR
Unit 11A

4-Ball Pendulum

(18 x 38)

KIENZLE CLOCK FACTORIES

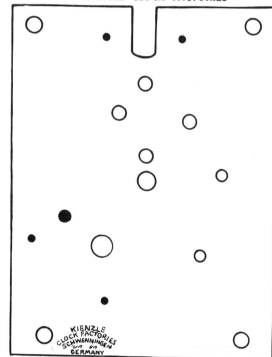

Plate 1385

4-Ball Pendulum
Pin Pallet Escapement
Lantern Pinions
USE .0035″ (.089mm) HOROLOVAR

(20 x 38)

KIENZLE CLOCK FACTORIES

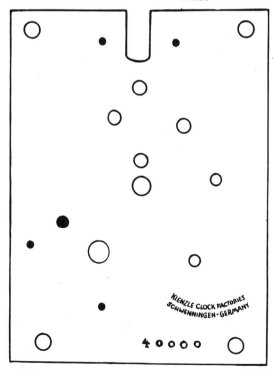

Plate 1387
Pin Pallet Escapement
Lantern Pinions
USE .0035″ (.089mm) HOROLOVAR

4-Ball Pendulum

(20 x 38)

K O

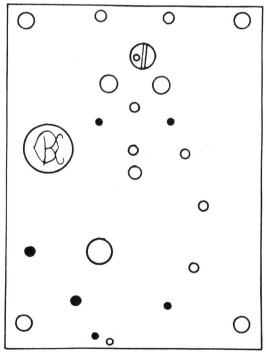

Plate 1388
USE .0032″ (.081mm) HOROLOVAR
Units 1, 3A

4-Ball Pendulum

(19 x 38)

K O

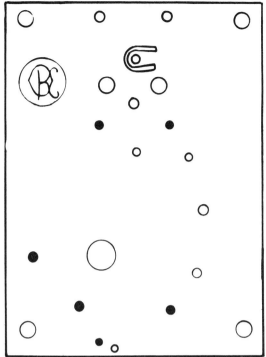

Plate 1389   4-Ball Pendulum
USE .0032″ (.081mm) HOROLOVAR
Units 1, 3A   (19 x 38)

K O

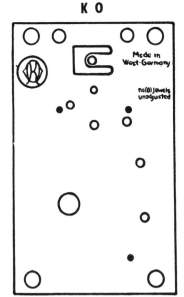

Plate 1390   1 Ball Pendulum
                              Miniature Clock
USE .0023″ (.058mm) HOROLOVAR
Units 5A, 5B, 5C, 5D, 5E   (14 x 30)

KOMA

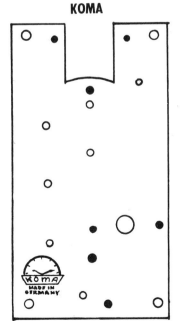

Plate 1392   4-Ball Pendulum
                              Miniature Clock
USE .003″ (.076mm) HOROLOVAR
Unit 14   (13 x 32)

KOMA

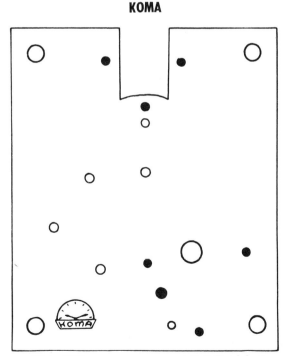

Plate 1393   4-Ball Pendulum
USE .0035″ (.089mm) HOROLOVAR
Units 13A, 13B   (20 x 38)

99

KOMA

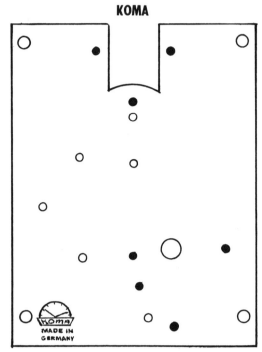

Plate 1393A   4-Ball Pendulum
USE .0035″ (.089mm) HOROLOVAR
Units 13A, 13B   (20 x 38)

KOMA

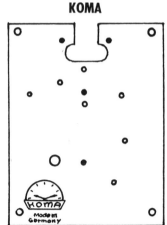

Plate 1393B   3-Ball Pendulum
      Pin Pallet Escapement
USE .0022″ (.056mm) HOROLOVAR
Unit 38   (12 x 25)

KONRAD MAUCH

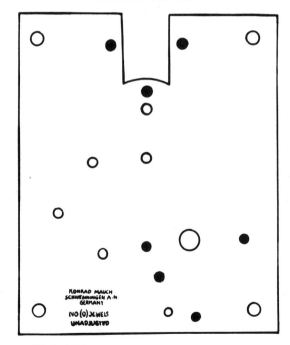

Plate 1394   4-Ball Pendulum
USE .0035″ (.089mm) HOROLOVAR
Units 13A, 13B   (20 x 38)

KONRAD MAUCH

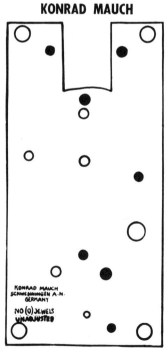

Plate 1395   4-Ball Pendulum
USE .0035″ (.089mm) HOROLOVAR
Units 13A, 13B   (20 x 38)

KONRAD MAUCH

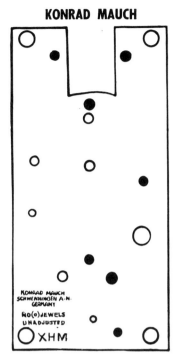

Plate 1395A 4-Ball Pendulum
USE .0035″ (.089mm) HOROLOVAR
Units 13A, 13B (20 x 38)

KONRAD MAUCH

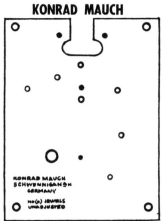

Plate 1396 3-Ball Pendulum
Pin Pallet Escapement
USE .0022″ (.056mm) HOROLOVAR
Unit 38 (12 x 25)

KONRAD MAUCH

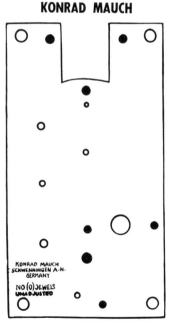

Plate 1399 4-Ball Pendulum
Miniature Clock
USE .0032″ (.081mm) HOROLOVAR
Unit 14 (13 x 32)

KONRAD MAUCH

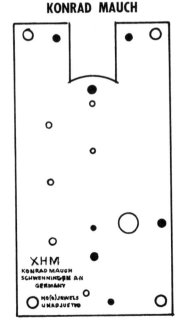

Plate 1399A 4-Ball Pendulum
Miniature Clock
USE .003″ (.076mm) HOROLOVAR
Unit 14 (13 x 32)

101

K S

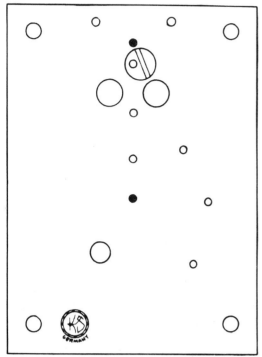

Plate 1404
USE .0036″ (.091mm) HOROLOVAR
Unit 11A

4-Ball Pendulum

(18 x 38)

K S

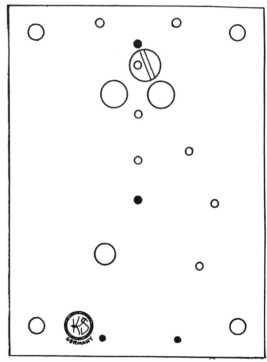

Plate 1404A
USE .0036″ (.091mm) HOROLOVAR
Unit 11B

4-Ball Pendulum

(18 x 38)

K S

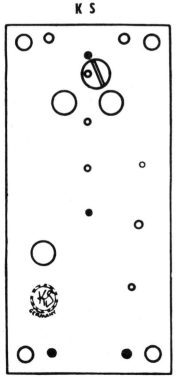

Plate 1405
USE .0036″ (.091mm) HOROLOVAR
Unit 11B

4-Ball Pendulum

(18 x 38)

K S

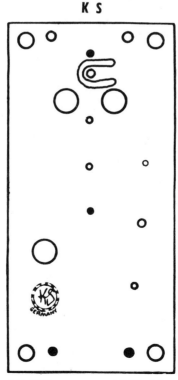

Plate 1405A
USE .0036″ (.091mm) HOROLOVAR
Unit 11B

4-Ball Pendulum

(18 x 38)

K S

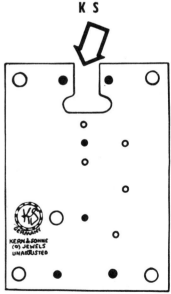

Plate 1406
USE .002″ (.051mm) HOROLOVAR
Unit 12A, 12B, 12C
USE .0019″ (.048mm) HOROLOVAR
Unit 12D

4-Ball Pendulum
Miniature Clock

(12 x 25)

102

K S

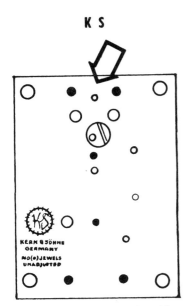

K S

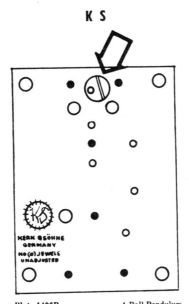

K S

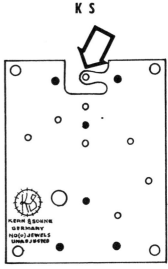

Plate 1406A   4-Ball Pendulum
                            Miniature Clock
USE .002″ (.051mm) HOROLOVAR
Units 12A, 12B, 12C
USE .0019″ (.048mm) HOROLOVAR
Unit 12D   (12 x 25)

Plate 1406B   4-Ball Pendulum
                            Miniature Clock
USE .002″ (.051mm) HOROLOVAR
Units 12A, 12B, 12C
USE .0019″ (.048mm) HOROLOVAR
Unit 12D   (12 x 25)

Plate 1406C   4-Ball or Disc Pendulum
                              Midget Clock
                        Pin Pallet Escapement
USE .002″ (.051mm) HOROLOVAR
Unit 12E   (14 x 25)

K S

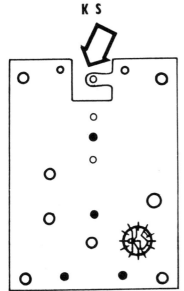

KUNDO

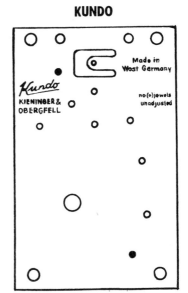

Plate 1406F   4-Ball Pendulum
                            Miniature Clock
USE .0019″ (.048mm) HOROLOVAR
Unit 12D   (12 x 25)

Plate 1406 H   4-Ball Pendulum
USE .0023″ (.058mm) HOROLOVAR
Unit 5E
USE .0022″— (.056mm—) HOROLOVAR
Unit 5F   (14 x 30)

KUNDO

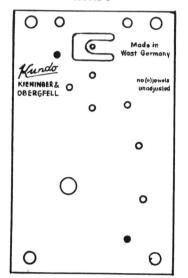

Plate 1407A   4-Ball Pendulum
USE .0023″ (.058mm) HOROLOVAR
Unit 5E
USE .0022″— (.056mm—) HOROLOVAR
Unit 5F   (14 x 30)

KUNDO

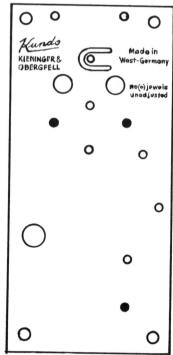

Plate 1407B   4-Ball Pendulum
USE .0032″ (.081mm) HOROLOVAR
Units 3A, 3B, 3C   (19 x 38)

KUNDO

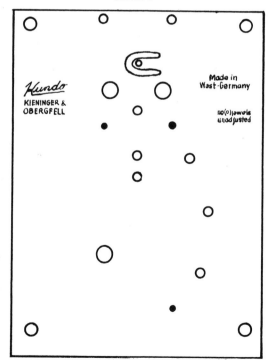

Plate 1407D   4-Ball Pendulum
USE .0032″ (.081mm) HOROLOVAR
Unit 3C   (19 x 38)

KUNDO

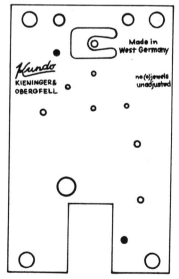

Plate 1407H   4-Ball Pendulum
USE .0023″ (.058mm) HOROLOVAR
Unit 5E
USE .0022″— (.056mm—) HOROLOVAR
Unit 5F   (14 x 30)

L. HERR SOHNE

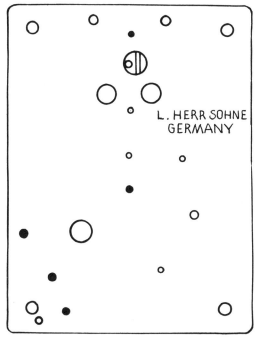

Plate 1408   4-Ball Pendulum
USE .004″ (.102mm) HOROLOVAR
Unit 27A   (19 x 36)

L. von der Burg G.m.b.H.

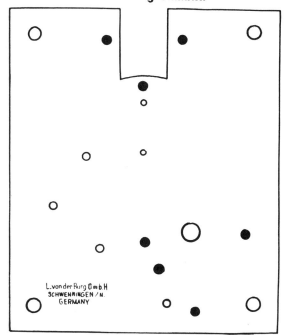

Plate 1409   4-Ball Pendulum
USE .0035″ (.089mm) HOROLOVAR
Units 13A, 13B   (20 x 38)

L. von der Burg

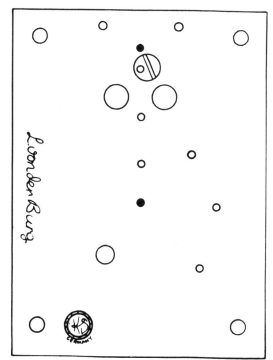

Plate 1411   4-Ball Pendulum
USE .0036″ (.091mm) HOROLOVAR
Unit 11A   (18 x 38)

Made in Germany

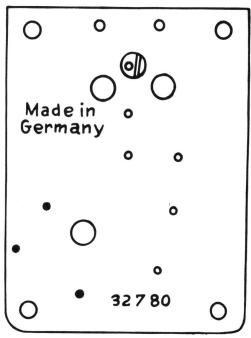

Plate 1415   Chronometer Balance
"Temperature Compensating" Pendulum
USE .0045″— (.114mm—) HOROLOVAR
                          (19 x 36)

Made in Germany

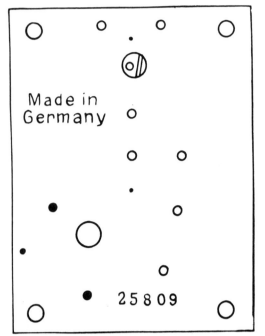

Plate 1419 Disc Pendulum
USE .0045"* (.114mm*) HOROLOVAR
(19 x 36)

MADE IN GERMANY

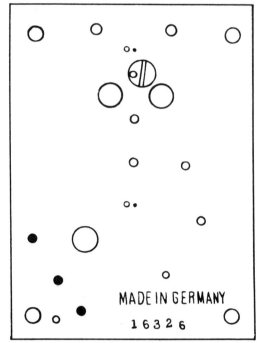

Plate 1423 Disc Pendulum
USE .0038" (.097mm) HOROLOVAR
(19 x 36)

MADE IN GERMANY

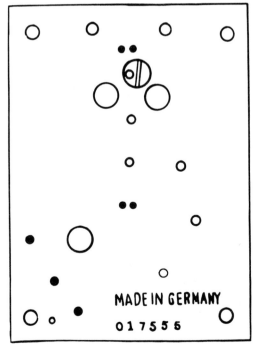

Plate 1427 Disc Pendulum
USE .0038" (.097mm) HOROLOVAR
(19 x 36)

106

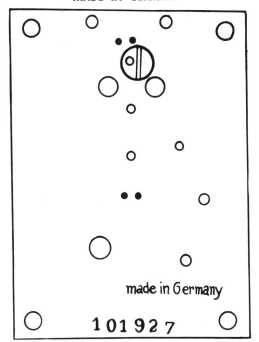

MADE IN GERMANY

made in Germany

101927

Plate 1431   Disc Pendulum
USE .0038″ (.097mm) HOROLOVAR
                    (18 x 38)

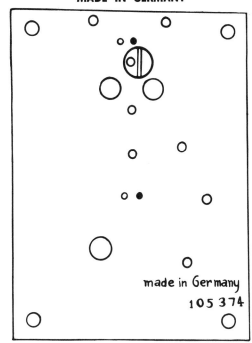

MADE IN GERMANY

made in Germany

105374

Plate 1435   Disc Pendulum
USE .0038″ (.097mm) HOROLOVAR
                    (18 x 38)

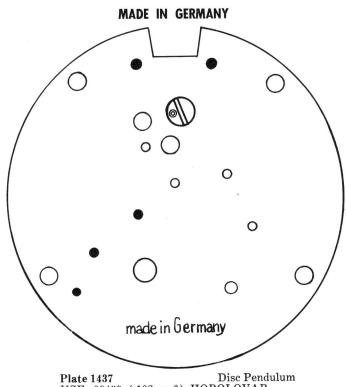

MADE IN GERMANY

made in Germany

Plate 1437   Disc Pendulum
USE .004″* (.102mm*) HOROLOVAR
                    (19 x 36)

MADE IN GERMANY

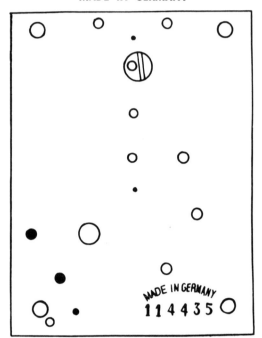

Plate 1439   4-Ball Pendulum
USE .004″ (.102mm) HOROLOVAR
      (19 x 36)

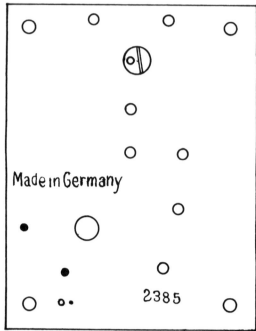

Plate 1441   Disc Pendulum
USE .004″ (.102mm) HOROLOVAR
      (19 x 38)

MADE IN GERMANY

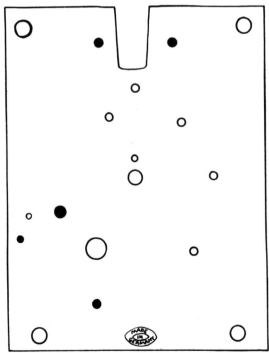

Plate 1443   Disc Pendulum
USE .004″* (.102mm*) HOROLOVAR
      (19 x 38)

MADE IN GERMANY

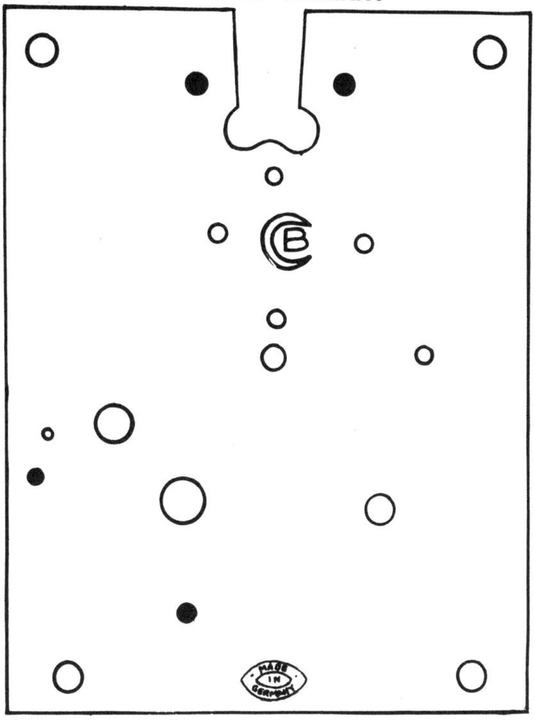

MADE IN GERMANY

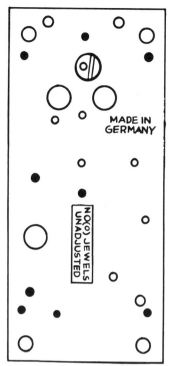

Plate 1444
USE .0045"— (.114mm—) HOROLOVAR

Disc Pendulum
Lantern Pinions
(20 x 38)

Plate 1447
USE .004" (.102mm) HOROLOVAR
Unit 26

4-Ball Pendulum

(19 x 36)

NO(O)JEWELS
UNADJUSTED

MADE IN GERMANY

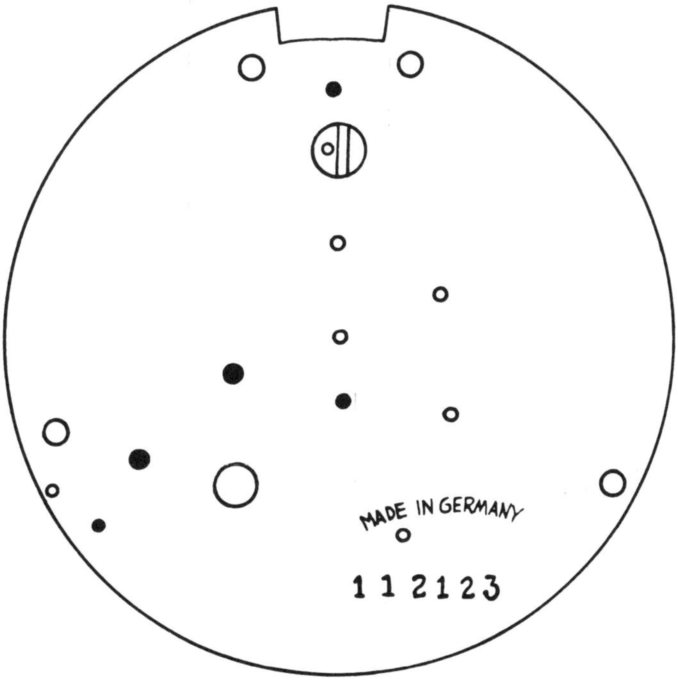

MADE IN GERMANY

1 1 2 1 2 3

Plate 1451
USE .0045" (.114mm) HOROLOVAR

Disc Pendulum

(19 x 36)

109

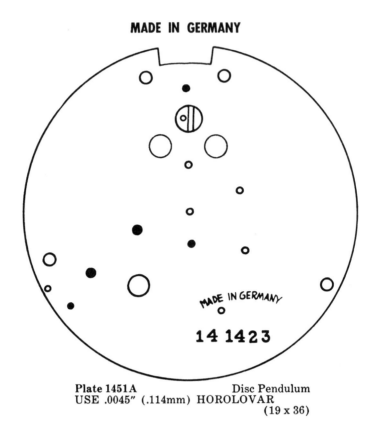

MADE IN GERMANY

MADE IN GERMANY

14 1423

Plate 1451A   Disc Pendulum
USE .0045″ (.114mm) HOROLOVAR
(19 x 36)

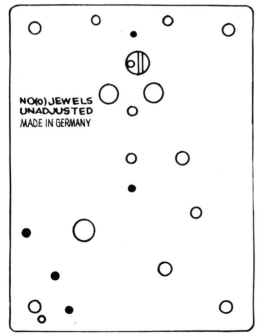

MADE IN GERMANY

NO(0) JEWELS
UNADJUSTED
MADE IN GERMANY

Plate 1453   4-Ball Pendulum
USE .004″ (.102mm) HOROLOVAR
Unit 27A   (19 x 36)

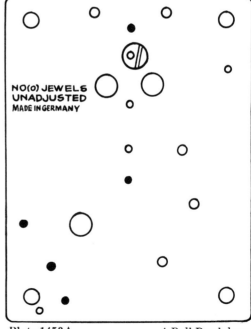

MADE IN GERMANY

NO(0) JEWELS
UNADJUSTED
MADE IN GERMANY

Plate 1453A   4-Ball Pendulum
Hour Striker
USE .004″ (.102mm) HOROLOVAR
Unit 27A   (19 x 36)

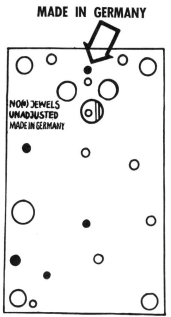

Plate 1455   Miniature Movement
Standard 4-Ball Pendulum
USE .003″ (.076mm) HOROLOVAR
Units 22, 23A, 24   (16 x 36)

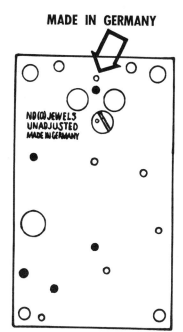

Plate 1455A   Standard 4-Ball Pendulum
Miniature Movement
USE .0032″ (.081mm) HOROLOVAR
Unit 23B   (16 x 36)

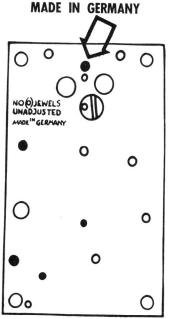

Plate 1456   4-Ball Pendulum
Miniature Clock
USE .0025″ (.064mm) HOROLOVAR
Units 28A, 28B   (16 x 36)

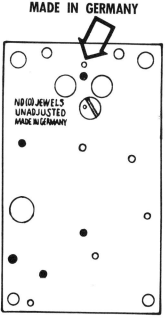

Plate 1457   4-Ball Pendulum
Miniature Clock
USE .0028″ (.071mm) HOROLOVAR
Unit 28C   (16 x 36)

MADE IN GERMANY

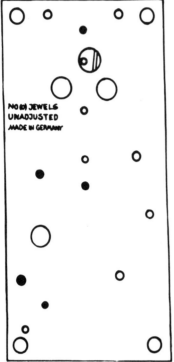

Plate 1458   4-Ball Pendulum
Dome Clock
USE .0035″ (.089mm) HOROLOVAR
Units 19, 20A, 21
Square Clock
USE .0033″ (.084mm) HOROLOVAR
Unit 20B   (19 x 36)

MADE IN GERMANY

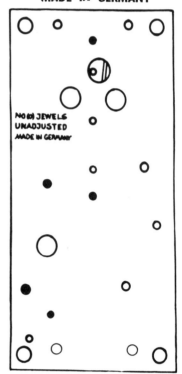

Plate 1460   4-Ball Pendulum
USE .0035″ (.089mm) HOROLOVAR
Units 19, 20A, 21
USE .0038″ (.097mm) HOROLOVAR
Unit 27B   (19 x 36)

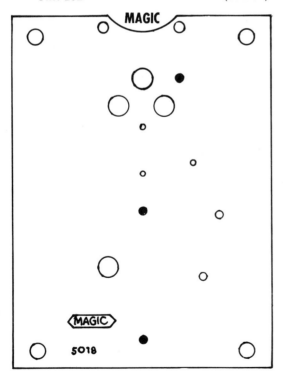

Plate 1461   4-Ball Pendulum
USE .004″ (.102mm) HOROLOVAR
           (19 x 38)

MARSHALL FIELD & CO.

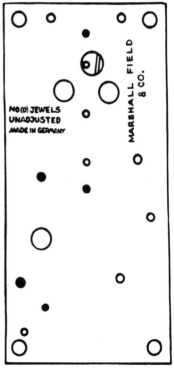

Plate 1461B   4-Ball Pendulum
USE .0035″ (.089mm) HOROLOVAR
Units 19, 20A, 21
USE .0038″ (.097mm) HOROLOVAR
Unit 27B   (19 x 36)

MASTER

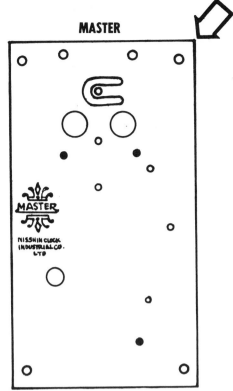

Plate 1461C   4-Ball Pendulum
USE .0035″ (.089mm) HOROLOVAR
Units 41A, 41B   (19 x 38)

MASTER

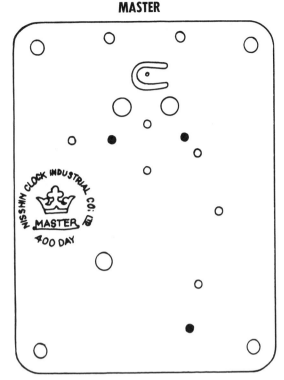

Plate 1461D   4-Ball Pendulum
USE .0034″ (.077mm) HOROLOVAR
Unit 45, 45A   (19 x 38)

MASTER

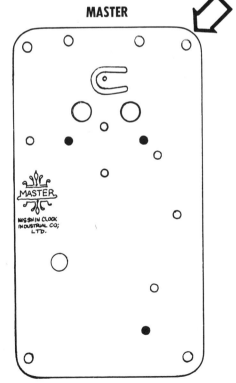

Plate 1461E   4-Ball Pendulum
USE .0034″ (.077mm) HOROLOVAR
Unit 45, 45A   (19 x 38)

MAUCH-FRICK

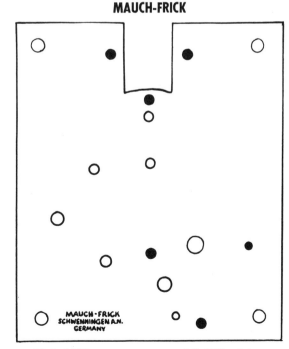

Plate 1462   4-Ball Pendulum
USE .0035″ (.089mm) HOROLOVAR
Units 13A, 13B   (20 x 38)

MAX LANDAU & CO. INC.

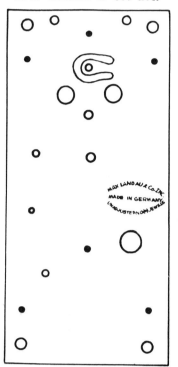

MAX LANDAU & Co. INC.
MADE IN GERMANY
UNADJUSTED NO JEWELS

Plate 1463   4-Ball Pendulum
USE .0037″ (.094mm) HOROLOVAR
Units 16, 17   (19 x 38)

MAYER

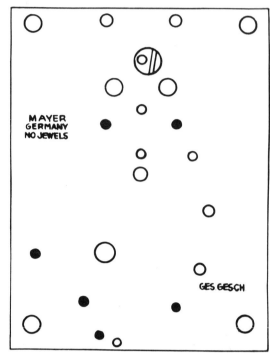

MAYER
GERMANY
NO JEWELS

GES GESCH

Plate 1467   4-Ball Pendulum
USE .0032″ (.081mm) HOROLOVAR
Units 1, 3A   (19 x 38)

METASCO INC.

METASCO INC.
NO(0) JEWELS
UNADJUSTED
MADE IN GERMANY

Plate 1468   4-Ball Pendulum
USE .0037″ (.094mm) HOROLOVAR
Units 16, 17   (19 x 38)

MOHERTUS TRADING CO.

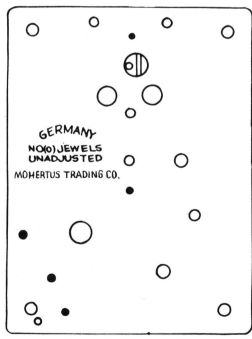

GERMANY
NO(0) JEWELS
UNADJUSTED
MOHERTUS TRADING CO.

Plate 1469   4-Ball Pendulum
USE .004″ (.102mm) HOROLOVAR
Unit 27A   (19 x 36)

NEUECK

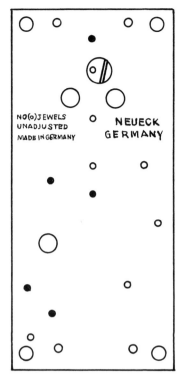

Plate 1469C   4-Ball Pendulum
USE .0036″ (.091mm) HOROLOVAR
Unit 27C   (19 x 36)

NISSHIN

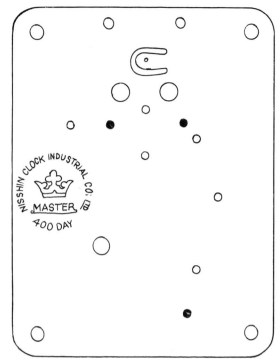

Plate 1469D   4-Ball Pendulum
USE .0034″ (.077mm) HOROLOVAR
Unit 45, 45A   (19 x 38)

NISSHIN

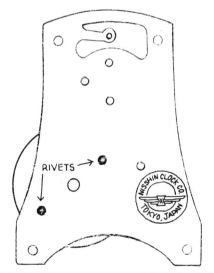

Plate 1469E   4-Ball Pendulum
USE .0028″ (.071mm) HOROLOVAR
Unit 46, 46A   (12 x 32)

NO (0) JEWELS
(Plate marking error)

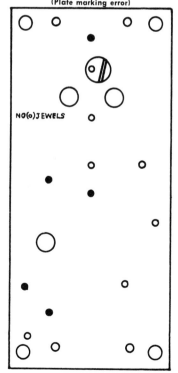

Plate 1469F   3-Ball Pendulum
USE .0036″ (.091mm) HOROLOVAR
Unit 27C   (19 x 36)

OSCAR HEYMANN

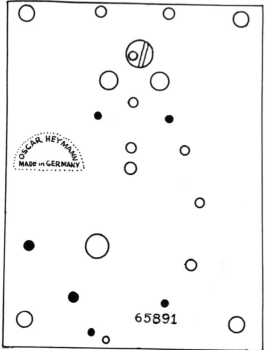

Plate 1470
USE .0032″ (.081mm) HOROLOVAR
Units 1, 3A

4-Ball Pendulum

(19 x 38)

PATENT ANGEMELDET

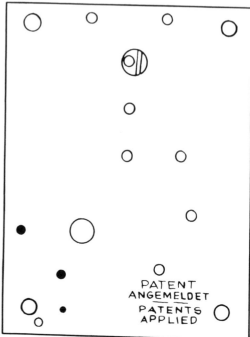

Plate 1471
USE .004″ (.102mm) HOROLOVAR

Disc Pendulum

(19 x 38)

PENDULE 400 JOURS

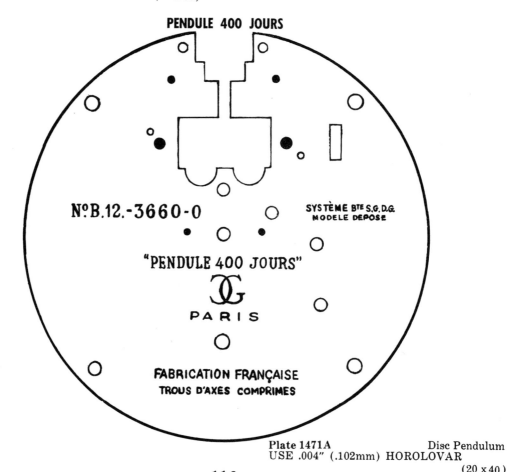

Plate 1471A
USE .004″ (.102mm) HOROLOVAR

Disc Pendulum

(20 x 40)

116

PERFECTA WATCH & CLOCK CO.

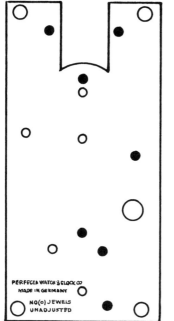

Plate 1471B 4-Ball Pendulum
USE .0035" (.089mm) HOROLOVAR
Units 13A, 13B (20 x 38)

PERFECTA WATCH & CLOCK CO.

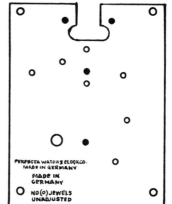

Plate 1471C 3-Ball Pendulum
Pin Pallet Escapement
USE .0022" (.056mm) HOROLOVAR
Unit 38 (12 x 25)

PERFECTA WATCH & CLOCK CO.

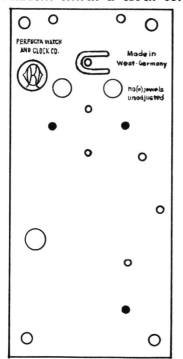

Plate 1471D 4-Ball Pendulum
USE .0032" (.081mm) HOROLOVAR
Unit 3A (19 x 38)

PERFECTA WATCH & CLOCK CO.

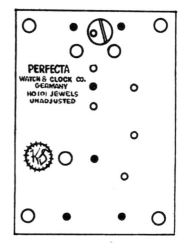

Plate 1471E 4-Ball Pendulum
Miniature Clock
USE .002" (.051mm)
Units 12A, 12B, 12C
USE .0019" (.048mm) HOROLOVAR
Unit 12D (12 x 25)

PETERSEN

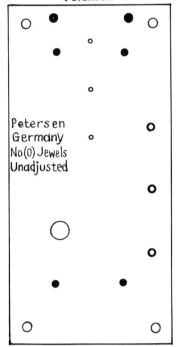

Petersen
Germany
No(0) Jewels
Unadjusted

Plate 1472   4-Ball Pendulum *or*
                            4-Figurine Pendulum
USE .0033" (.084mm) HOROLOVAR
Units 18B, 18C   (19 x 38)

P. R. MYERS & CO.

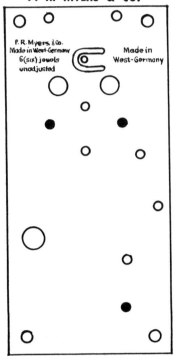

P. R. Myers & Co.
Made in West-Germany
6(six) jewels
unadjusted

Made in
West-Germany

Plate 1472E   4-Ball Pendulum
USE .0032" (.081mm) HOROLOVAR
Unit 3A   (19 x 38)

P. R. MYERS & CO.

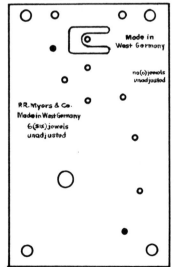

Made in
West Germany

no(o)jewels
unadjusted

P.R.Myers & Co.
Made in West Germany
6(six)jewels
unadjusted

Plate 1472F   4-Ball Pendulum
USE .0023" (.058mm) HOROLOVAR
Unit 5E
USE .0022" — (.056mm —) HOROLOVAR
Unit 5F   (14 x 30)

R

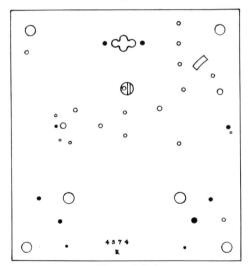

4574
R

(½ actual size)

Plate 1473   Disc Pendulum
Hour and Half Hour Gong Strike
USE .0045" — (.114mm —) HOROLOVAR

(½ actual size)

Plate 1479   Disc Pendulum
Hour and Half Hour Bell Strike
USE .005" — (.127mm —) HOROLOVAR

R

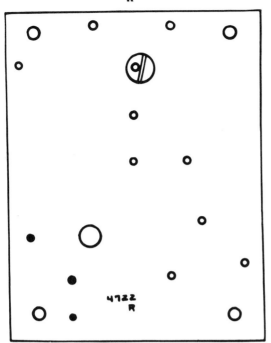

Plate 1475 Disc Pendulum
USE .0038″ (.097mm) HOROLOVAR
(19 x 36)

RALPH HERMAN CLOCK HOUSE

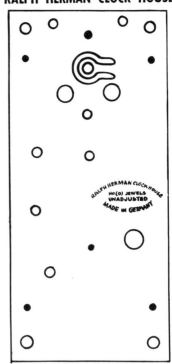

Plate 1477 4-Ball Pendulum
USE .0037″ (.094mm) HOROLOVAR
Units 16, 17 (19 x 38)

RENSIE WATCH CO. INC.

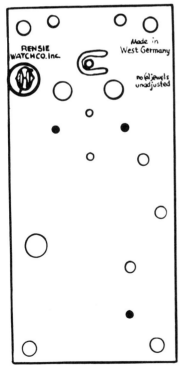

Plate 1479 4-Ball Pendulum
USE .0032″ (.081mm) HOROLOVAR
Units 1, 3A, 3B, 3C (19 x 38)

RENSIE WATCH CO. INC.

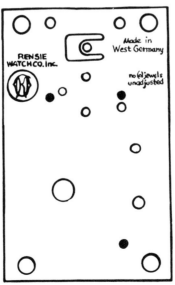

Plate 1483 4-Ball Pendulum
Miniature Clock
USE .0023″ (.058mm) HOROLOVAR
Units 5A, 5B, 5C, 5D, 5E (14 x 30)

REX

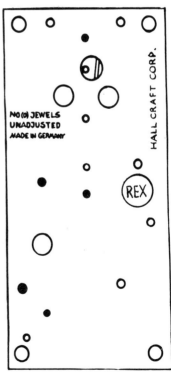

Plate 1484 4-Ball Pendulum
USE .0035″ (.089mm) HOROLOVAR
Units 19, 20A, 21
USE .0038″ (.097mm) HOROLOVAR
Unit 27B (19 x 36)

REX

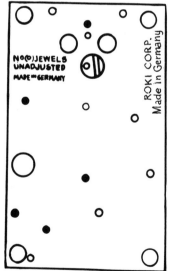

Plate 1484A   4-Ball Pendulum
Miniature Clock
USE .0025″ (.064mm) HOROLOVAR
Unit 28A, 28B   (16 x 36)

REX

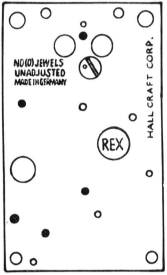

Plate 1484B   4-Ball Pendulum
Miniature Clock
USE .0028″ (.071mm) HOROLOVAR
Unit 28C   (16 x 36)

ROBANNE CORP.

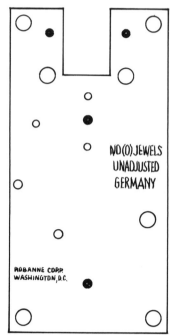

Plate 1485   4-Ball Pendulum
USE .0035″ (.089mm) HOROLOVAR
(18 x 38)

ROKI CORP.

Plate 1486   Standard 4-Ball Pendulum
Miniature Movement
USE .003″ (.076mm) HOROLOVAR
Units 22, 23A, 24   (16 x 36)

ROTH BROS.

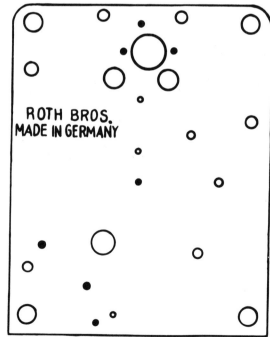

Plate 1487   4-Ball Pendulum
USE .0035″ (.089mm) HOROLOVAR
Unit 31   (19 x 38)

ROYAL CLOCK CORPORATION

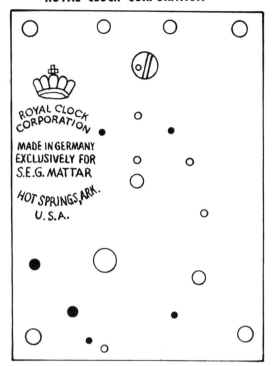

Plate 1491
USE .0032″ (.081mm) HOROLOVAR
Units 1, 3A

4-Ball Pendulum

(19 x 38)

ROYCE WATCH CO.

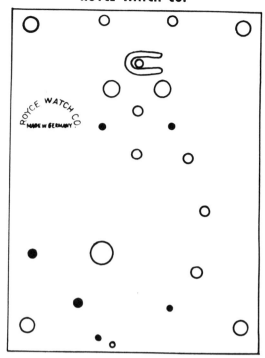

Plate 1495
USE .0032″ (.081mm) HOROLOVAR
Units 1, 3A

4-Ball Pendulum

(19 x 38)

ROYCE WATCH CO.

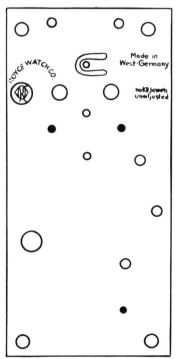

Plate 1499
USE .0032″ (.081mm) HOROLOVAR
Units 1, 3A, 3B, 3C

4-Ball Pendulum

(19 x 38)

ROYCE WATCH CO.

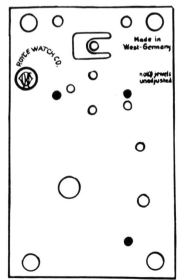

Plate 1503
USE .0023″ (.058mm) HOROLOVAR
Units 5A, 5B, 5C, 5D, 5E

4-Ball Pendulum
Miniature Clock

(14 x 30)

R S M

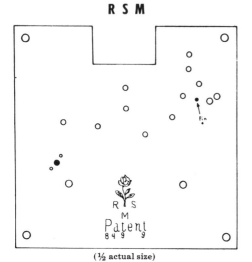

(½ actual size)

Plate 1504   3″ Ball Pendulum
Duplex Escapement
Hour and Half Hour Bell Strike
4½″ Suspension Spring
USE .0036″ (.091mm) HOROLOVAR

G

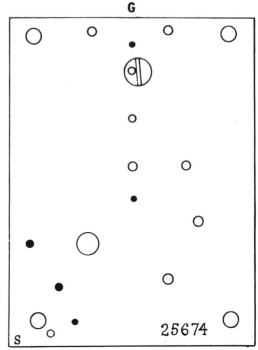

Plate 1504A   Disc Pendulum
7³⁄₁₆″ Suspension Spring
USE .005″— (.127mm—) HOROLOVAR
(19 x 36)

SCHLENKER & POSNER

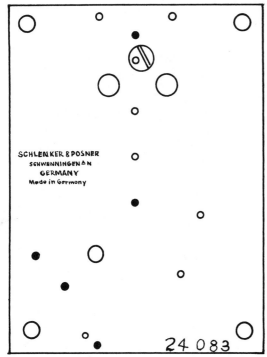

Plate 1505   4-Ball Pendulum
USE .004″ (.102mm) HOROLOVAR
(19 x 36)

SELSI

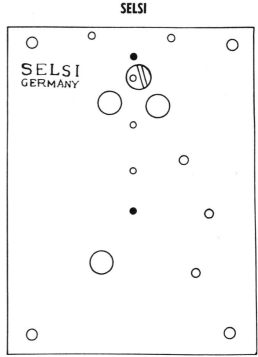

Plate 1507   4-Ball Pendulum
USE .0035″ (.089mm) HOROLOVAR
(18 x 38)

SELSI

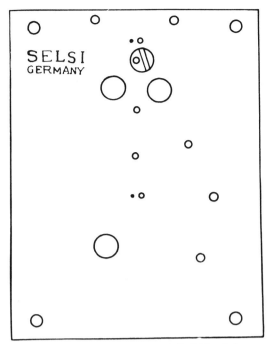

SELSI
GERMANY

Plate 1511   4-Ball Pendulum
USE .0035″ (.089mm) HOROLOVAR
                                    (18 x 38)

SELSI

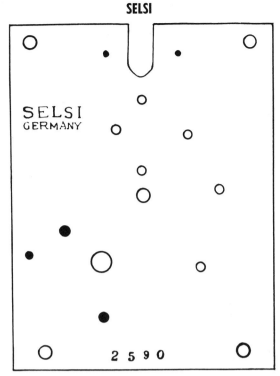

SELSI
GERMANY

2 5 9 0

Plate 1515   4-Ball Pendulum
                                    Lantern Pinions
USE .0035″ (.089mm) HOROLOVAR
                                    (20 x 38)

SEMESTER UHR.

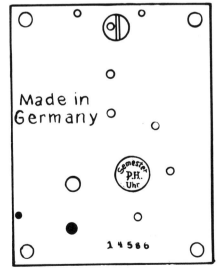

Made in
Germany

1 4 5 8 6

Plate 1519   Standard Disc Pendulum
                                  Miniature Movement
USE .004″ (.102mm) HOROLOVAR

123

S. HALLER

S.HALLER
SIMONSWALD

NO (O) JEWELS
UNADJUSTED
GERMANY

Plate 1520   4-Ball Pendulum
USE .0028″ (.071mm) HOROLOVAR
Unit 42   (18 x 38)

S. HALLER

S HALLER
SIMONSWALD

NO (O) JEWELS
UNADJUSTED
GERMANY

Plate 1521   4-Ball Pendulum
                 Miniature Clock
USE .0022″ (.056mm) HOROLOVAR
Unit 43   (12 x 24)

S. HALLER

S.HALLER
SIMONSWALD

NO (O) JEWELS
UNADJUSTED
GERMANY

Plate 1522   4-Ball Pendulum
                 Midget Clock
USE .0018″ (.046mm) HOROLOVAR
Unit 44   (12 x 24)

SOKOL MONTAG & CO.

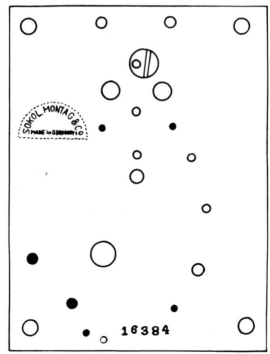

SOKOL MONTAG & CO.
MADE in GERMANY

16384

Plate 1523   4-Ball Pendulum
USE .0032″ (.081mm) HOROLOVAR
Units 1, 3A   (19 x 38)

SOKOL MONTAG & CO.

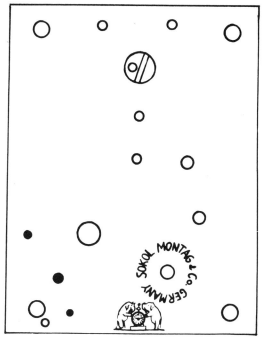

Plate 1527   4-Ball Pendulum
USE .004″ (.102mm) HOROLOVAR
Units 6, 7, 8, 9   (19 x 36)

SPECIALTY TRADING CO.

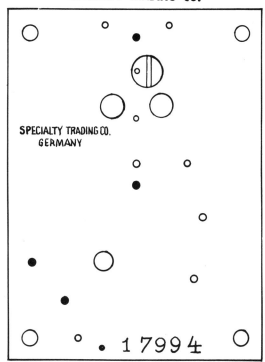

Plate 1529   4-Ball Pendulum
USE .0036″ (.091mm) HOROLOVAR
Unit 11B   (19 x 36)

THE CARP

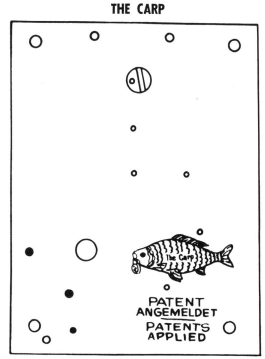

Plate 1531   Twin Loop "Temperature Compensating" Pendulum
USE .004″ (.102mm) HOROLOVAR
        (19 x 36)

THE GERSON CO.

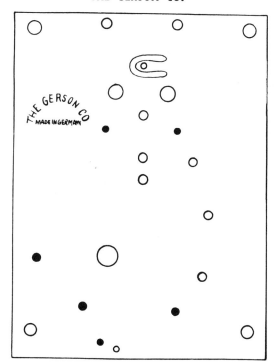

Plate 1533   4-Ball Pendulum
USE .0032″ (.081mm) HOROLOVAR
Units 1, 3A   (19 x 38)

THE J. L. HUDSON CO.

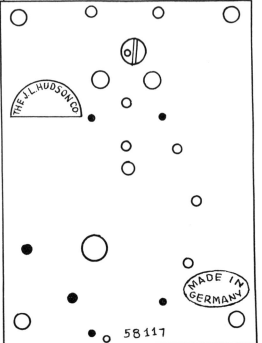

Plate 1534   4-Ball Pendulum
USE .0032″ (.081mm) HOROLOVAR
Units 1, 3A   (19 x 38)

THE J. L. HUDSON CO.

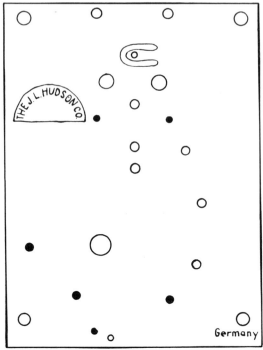

Plate 1535   4-Ball Pendulum
USE .0032″ (.081mm) HOROLOVAR
Units 1, 3A   (19 x 38)

THE J. L. HUDSON CO.

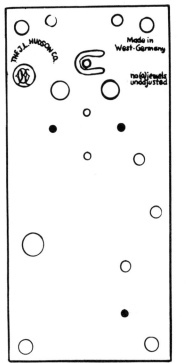

Plate 1539   4-Ball Pendulum
USE .0032″ (.081mm) HOROLOVAR
Units 1, 3A, 3B, 3C   (19 x 38)

THE J. L. HUDSON CO.

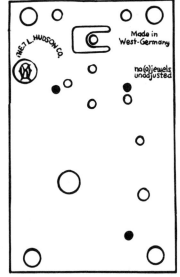

Plate 1543   4-Ball Pendulum
                            Miniature Clock
USE .0023″ (.058mm) HOROLOVAR
Units 5A, 5B, 5C, 5D, 5E   (14 x 30)

THE NATIONAL SILVER CO.

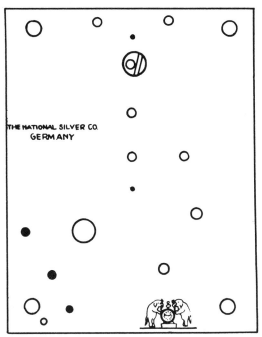

Plate 1547　　　　　　4-Ball Pendulum
USE .004″ (.102mm) HOROLOVAR
Units 6, 7, 8, 9　　　　　　(19 x 36)

THE NATIONAL SILVER CO.

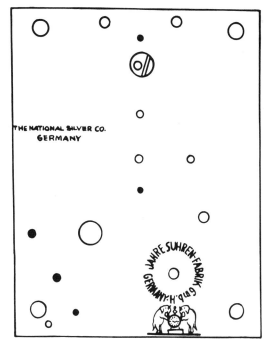

Plate 1551　　　　　　4-Ball Pendulum
USE .004″ (.102mm) HOROLOVAR
Units 6, 7, 8, 9　　　　　　(19 x 36)

THE NATIONAL SILVER CO.

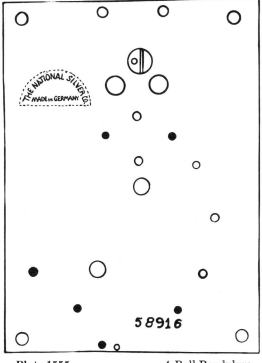

Plate 1555　　　　　　4-Ball Pendulum
USE .0032″ (.081mm) HOROLOVAR
Units 1, 3A　　　　　　(19 x 38)

THE NATIONAL SILVER CO.

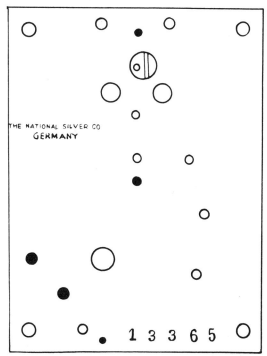

Plate 1559　　　　　　4-Ball Pendulum
USE .0035″* (.089mm*) HOROLOVAR
　　　　　　(19 x 38)

TRANSATLANTIC CLOCK CO.

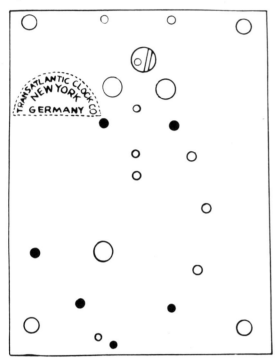

Plate 1563   4-Ball Pendulum
USE .0032″ (.081mm) HOROLOVAR
Units 1, 3A   (19 x 38)

UHRENFABRIK HERR

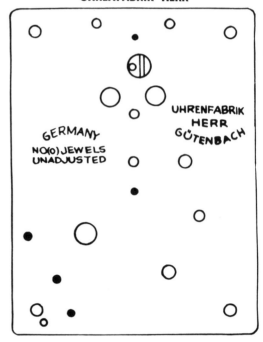

Plate 1567   4-Ball Pendulum
USE .004″ (.102mm) HOROLOVAR
Unit 27A   (19 x 36)

UHRENFABRIK HERR

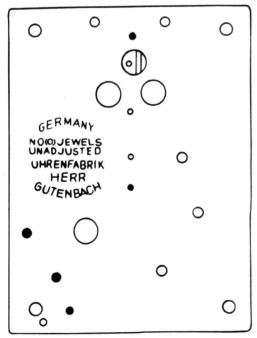

Plate 1571   4-Ball Pendulum
USE .004″ (.102mm) HOROLOVAR
Unit 27A   (19 x 36)

UHRENFABRIK HERR

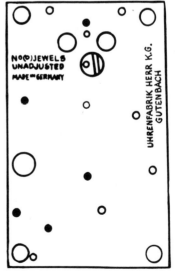

Plate 1572   4-Ball Pendulum
                                  Miniature Clock
USE .0025″ (.064mm) HOROLOVAR
Units 28A, 28B   (16 x 36)

UHRENFABRIK HERR

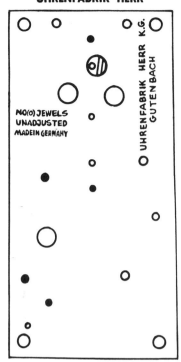

NO(0) JEWELS
UNADJUSTED
MADE IN GERMANY

UHRENFABRIK HERR K.G.
GUTENBACH

Plate 1572A   4-Ball Pendulum
USE .0038″ (.097mm) HOROLOVAR
Unit 27B   (19 x 36)

UHRENFABRIK K.G.

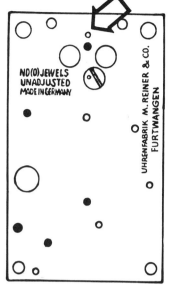

NO(0) JEWELS
UNADJUSTED
MADE IN GERMANY

UHRENFABRIK K.G.
GUTENBACH

Plate 1573   Miniature Movement
Standard 4-Ball Pendulum
USE .003″ (.076mm) HOROLOVAR
Units 22, 23A, 24   (16 x 36)

UHRENFABRIK M. REINER & CO.

NO(0) JEWELS
UNADJUSTED
MADE IN GERMANY

UHRENFABRIK M. REINER & CO.
FURTWANGEN

Plate 1574   Miniature Movement
Standard 4-Ball Pendulum
USE .0032″ (.081mm) HOROLOVAR
Unit 23B   (16 x 36)

UHRENFABRIK NEUECK

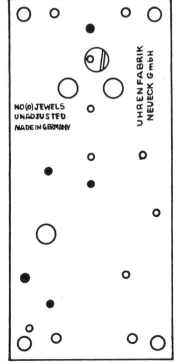

NO(0) JEWELS
UNADJUSTED
MADE IN GERMANY

UHRENFABRIK
NEUECK GmbH

Plate 1574B   4-Ball Pendulum
USE .0036″ (.091mm) HOROLOVAR
Unit 27C   (19 x 36)

URANIA

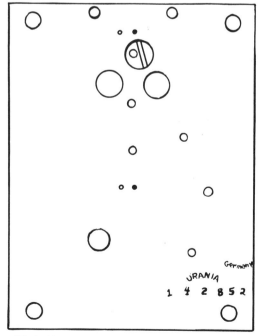

Germany

URANIA

1 4 2 8 5 2

Plate 1575   Disc Pendulum
USE .0025″ (.064mm) HOROLOVAR
     (18 x 38)

URANIA

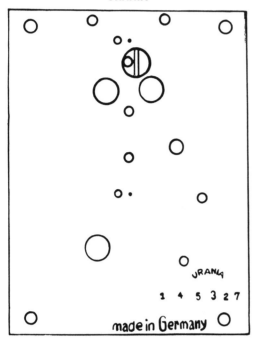

Plate 1579   Disc Pendulum
USE .0038″ (.097mm) HOROLOVAR
                              (18 x 38)

WELBY CORP.

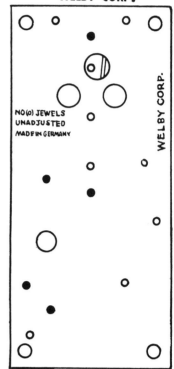

NO(0) JEWELS
UNADJUSTED
MADE IN GERMANY

Plate 1579A   4-Ball Pendulum
USE .0035″ (.089mm) HOROLOVAR
Units 19, 20A, 21
USE .0038″ (.097mm) HOROLOVAR
Unit 27B   (19 x 36)

WELBY CORPORATION

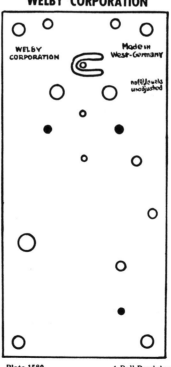

WELBY
CORPORATION

Made in
West-Germany

no(0)jewels
unadjusted

Plate 1580   4-Ball Pendulum
USE .0032″ (.081mm) HOROLOVAR
Units 1, 3A, 3B, 3C   (19 x 38)

WELBY CORP.

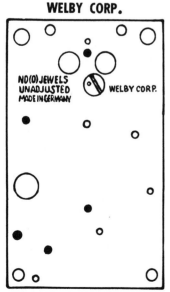

NO(0) JEWELS
UNADJUSTED
MADE IN GERMANY   WELBY CORP.

Plate 1579 B   Miniature Movement
          Standard 4-Ball Pendulum
USE .0032″ (.081mm) HOROLOVAR
Unit 23B   (16 x 36)

WELBY CORPORATION

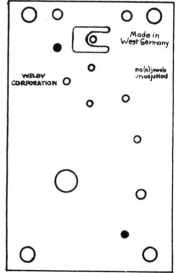

WELBY
CORPORATION

Made in
West Germany

no(0)jewels
unadjusted

Plate 1580A   4-Ball Pendulum
USE .0023″ (.058mm) HOROLOVAR
Unit 5E
USE .0022″ — (.056mm—) HOROLOVAR
Unit 5F   (14 x 30)

WELBY CORPORATION

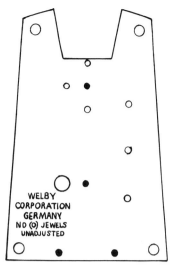

WELBY
CORPORATION
GERMANY
NO (0) JEWELS
UNADJUSTED

Plate 1581   4-Ball Pendulum
USE .0022″ (.056mm) HOROLOVAR
Unit 25B   (13 x 30)

WELBY CORPORATION

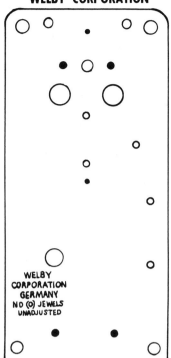

WELBY
CORPORATION
GERMANY
NO (0) JEWELS
UNADJUSTED

Plate 1581A   4-Ball Pendulum
USE .0033″ (.084mm) HOROLOVAR
Unit 25A   (18 x 38)

WILHELM V. MAIER

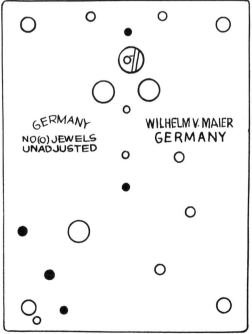

GERMANY
NO(0) JEWELS
UNADJUSTED

WILHELM V. MAIER
GERMANY

Plate 1582   4-Ball Pendulum
USE .004″ (.102mm) HOROLOVAR
Unit 27A   (19 x 36)

WILHELM V. MAIER

GERMANY
NO(0) JEWELS
UNADJUSTED

WILHELM V. MAIER
GERMANY

Plate 1582A   Standard 4-Ball Pendulum
                    Miniature Movement
USE .003″ (.076mm) HOROLOVAR
Units 22, 23A, 24   (16 x 36)

WILHELM V. MAIER

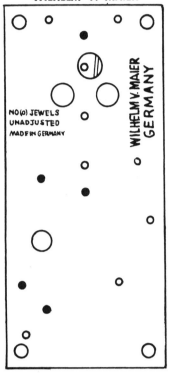

NO(0) JEWELS
UNADJUSTED
MADE IN GERMANY

WILHELM V. MAIER
GERMANY

Plate 1582AA   4-Ball Pendulum
USE .0035″ (.089mm) HOROLOVAR
Units 19, 20A, 21
USE .0038″ (.097mm) HOROLOVAR
Unit 27B   (19 x 36)

WILHELM V. MAIER

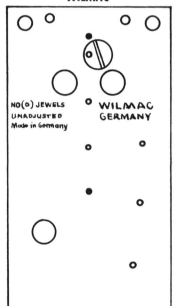

WILHELM V. MAIER
MADE IN GERMANY

NO(0) JEWELS
UNADJUSTED

Plate 1582B   3-Ball Pendulum
Pin Pallet Escapement
USE .0022″ (.056mm) HOROLOVAR
Unit 38   (12 x 25)

WILMAC

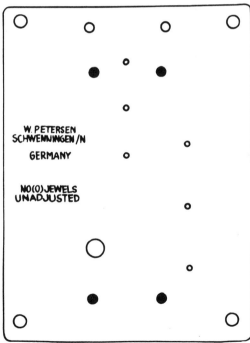

NO(0) JEWELS
UNADJUSTED
Made in Germany

WILMAC
GERMANY

Plate 1582C   4-Ball Pendu
USE .0036″ (.091mm) HOROLOVAR
Unit 11B   (18 x

WILMAC

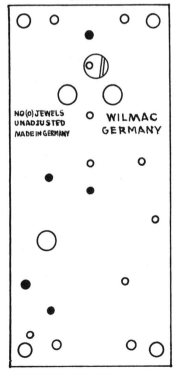

NO(0) JEWELS
UNADJUSTED
MADE IN GERMANY

WILMAC
GERMANY

Plate 1582D   4-Ball Pendulum
USE .0036″ (.091mm) HOROLOVAR
Unit 27C   (19 x 36)

W. PETERSEN

W. PETERSEN
SCHWENNINGEN /N

GERMANY

NO(0) JEWELS
UNADJUSTED

Plate 1583   4-Ball Pendulum
Standard Clock
USE .0033″ (.084mm) HOROLOVAR
Units 18B, 18C
Calendar Clock
USE .0036″ (.091mm) HOROLOVAR
Units 36A, 36B   (19 x 38)

WURTHNER WESTERN

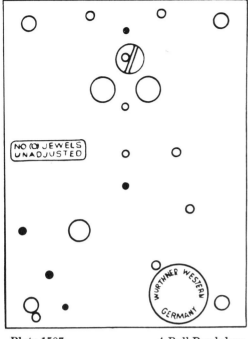

NO (O) JEWELS
UNADJUSTED

WURTHNER WESTERN
GERMANY

Plate 1587 4-Ball Pendulum
USE .004″ (.102mm) HOROLOVAR
Unit 26 (19 x 36)

WURTHNER WESTERN

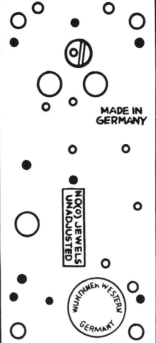

MADE IN
GERMANY

NO(O) JEWELS
UNADJUSTED

WURTHNER WESTERN
GERMANY

Plate 1591 4-Ball Pendulum
USE .004″ (.102mm) HOROLOVAR
Unit 26 (19 x 36)

WURTHNER WESTERN

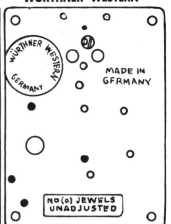

WURTHNER WESTERN
GERMANY

MADE IN
GERMANY

NO (O) JEWELS
UNADJUSTED

Plate 1593 4-Ball Pendulum
Midget Clock
USE .002″ (.051mm) HOROLOVAR
Unit 37 (9.5 x 27)

X H M

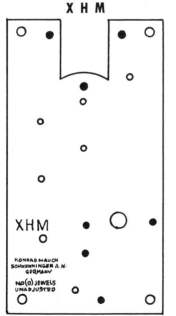

XHM

KONRAD MAUCH
SCHWENNINGEN A.N.
GERMANY

NO (O) JEWELS
UNADJUSTED

Plate 1594 4-Ball Pendulum
Miniature Clock
USE .003″ (.076mm) HOROLOVAR
Unit 14 (13 x 32)

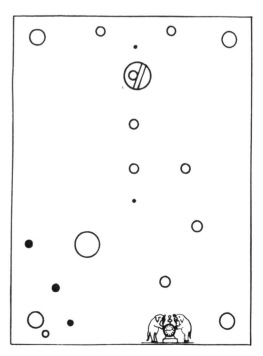

Plate 1595 4-Ball Pendulum
USE .004″ (.102mm) HOROLOVAR
Units 6, 7, 8, 9 (19 x 36)

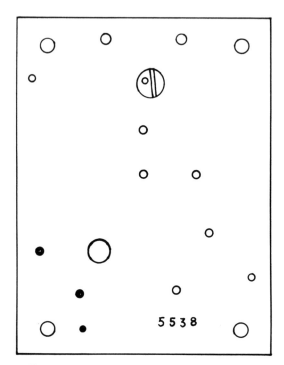

Plate 1597   Disc Pendulum
USE .0035″ (.089mm) HOROLOVAR
                                  (19 x 36)

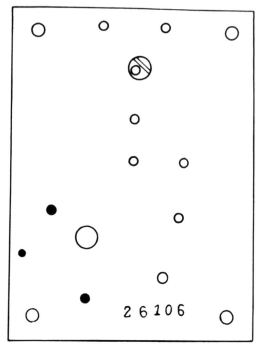

Plate 1599   Disc Pendulum
USE .0037″ (.094mm) HOROLOVAR
                                  (19 x 36)

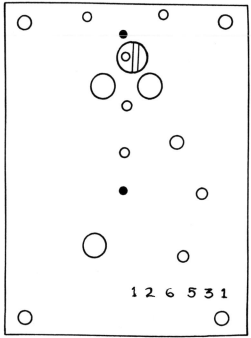

Plate 1601   4-Ball Pendulum
USE .0036″ (.091mm) HOROLOVAR
Unit 11A   (18 x 38)

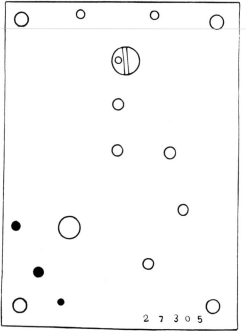

Plate 1603   Disc Pendulum
USE .004″* (.102mm*) HOROLOVAR
                                  (19 x 36)

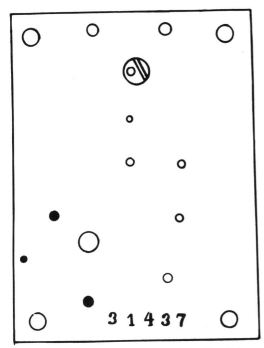

Plate 1607　　　　　　　　Disc Pendulum
USE .0038″ (.097mm) HOROLOVAR
　　　　　　　　　　　　　　　(19 x 36)

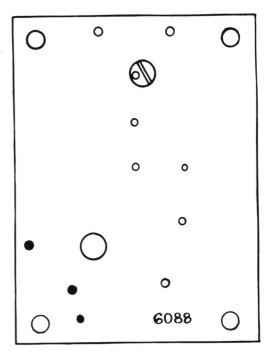

Plate 1610　　　　　　　　Disc Pendulum
USE .0038″ (.097mm) HOROLOVAR
　　　　　　　　　　　　　　　(19 x 36)

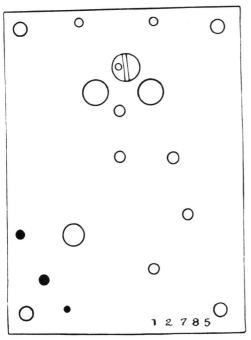

Plate 1613　　　　　　　　Disc Pendulum
USE .004″* (.102mm*) HOROLOVAR
　　　　　　　　　　　　　　　(19 x 36)

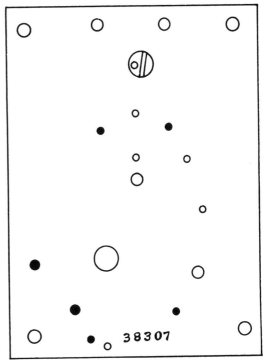

Plate 1615　　　　　　　　4-Ball Pendulum
USE .0032″ (.081mm) HOROLOVAR
Units 1, 3A
　　　　　　　　　　　　　　　(19 x 38)

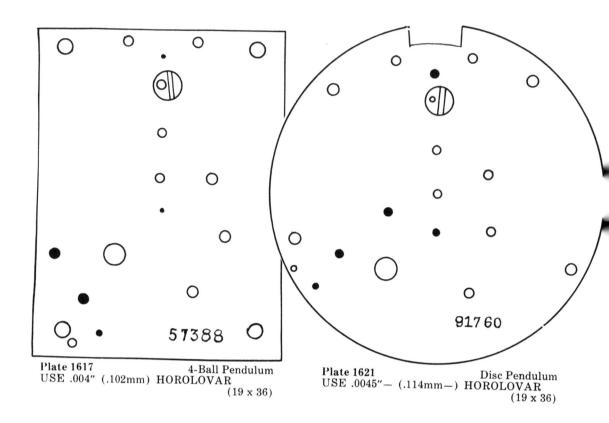

Plate 1617 4-Ball Pendulum
USE .004″ (.102mm) HOROLOVAR
(19 x 36)

57388

Plate 1621 Disc Pendulum
USE .0045″— (.114mm—) HOROLOVAR
(19 x 36)

91760

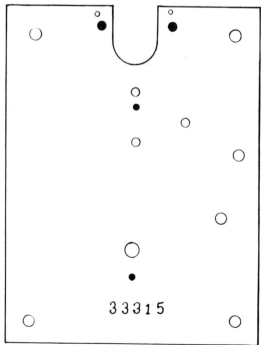

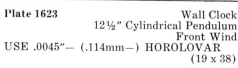

Plate 1623 Wall Clock
12½″ Cylindrical Pendulum
Front Wind
USE .0045″— (.114mm—) HOROLOVAR
(19 x 38)

33315

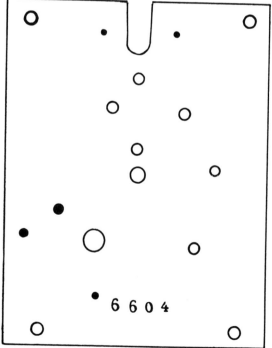

Plate 1627 4-Ball Pendulum
Pin Pallet Escapement
Lantern Pinions
USE .0035″ (.089mm) HOROLOVAR
(20 x 38)

6604

136

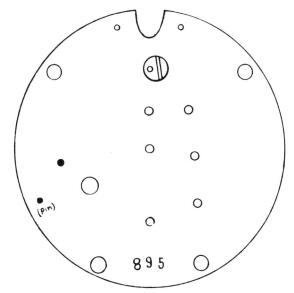

Plate 1631 Disc Pendulum
Miniature Clock
8″ High Square Case
USE .0025″ (.064mm) HOROLOVAR

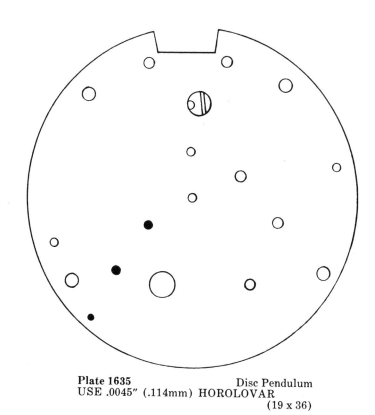

Plate 1635 Disc Pendulum
USE .0045″ (.114mm) HOROLOVAR
(19 x 36)

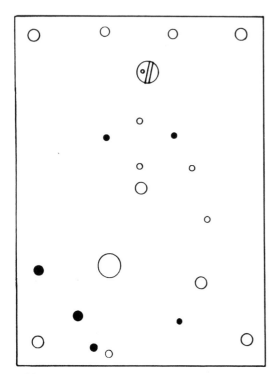

Plate 1639   4-Ball Pendulum
USE .0032″ (.081mm) HOROLOVAR
Units 1, 3A   (19 x 38)

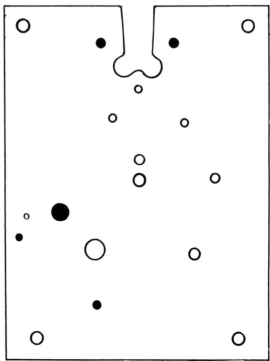

Plate 1643   3-Ball Pendulum
Pin Pallet Escapement
Lantern Pinions
USE .0035″ (.089mm) HOROLOVAR
(20 x 38)

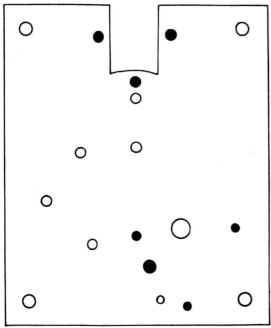

Plate 1647   4-Ball Pendulum
USE .0035″ (.089mm) HOROLOVAR
Units 13A, 13B   (20 x 38)

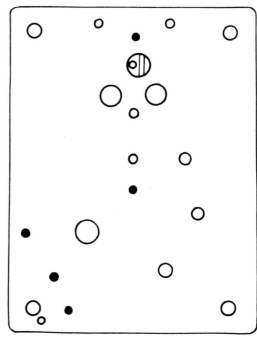

Plate 1651   4-Ball Pendulum
USE .004″ (.102mm) HOROLOVAR
Unit 27A   (19 x 36)

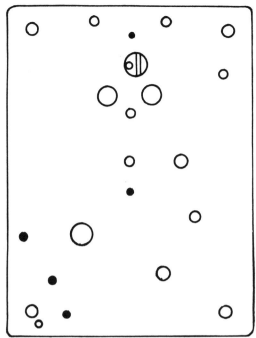

Plate 1652 4-Ball Pendulum
Hour Striker
USE .004″ (.102mm) HOROLOVAR
Unit 27A (19 x 36)

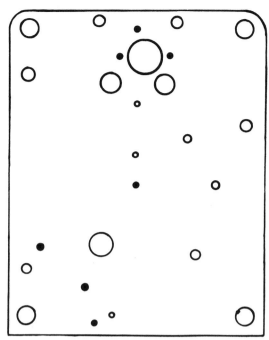

Plate 1659 4-Ball Pendulum
USE .0035″ (.089mm) HOROLOVAR
Unit 31 (19 x 38)

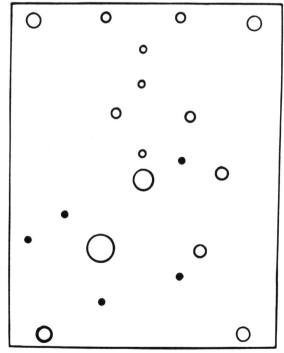

Plate 1663 4-Ball Pendulum
Pin Pallet Escapement
USE .0037″ (.094mm) HOROLOVAR
(20 x 38)

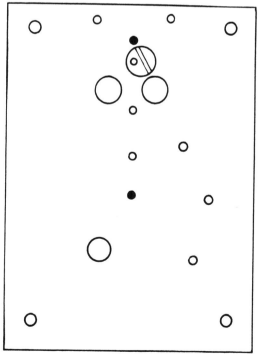

Plate 1667 Disc Pendulum
4-Ball Pendulum
USE .0036″ (.091mm) HOROLOVAR
Unit 11A (18 x 38)

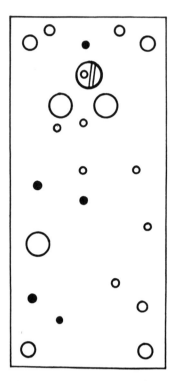

Plate 1669 4-Ball Pendulum
USE .004″ (.102mm) HOROLOVAR
Unit 26 (19 x 36)

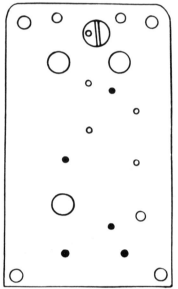

Plate 1671 4-Ball Pendulum
Miniature Clock
USE .0023″ (.058mm) HOROLOVAR
Units 29A, 29B (19 x 32)

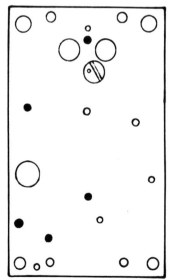

Plate 1672 4-Ball Pendulum
Miniature Clock
USE .0028″ (0.71mm) HOROLOVAR
Unit 28C (16 x 36)

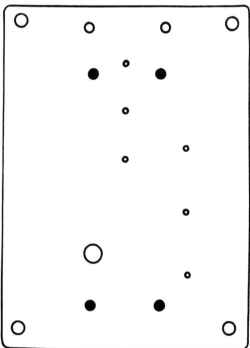

Plate 1673 4-Ball Pendulum
USE .0033″ (.084mm) HOROLOVAR
Units 18B, 18C (19 x 38)

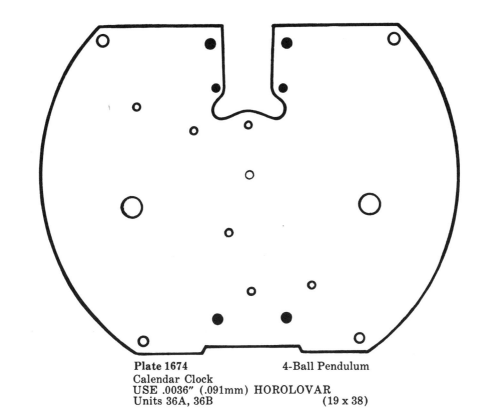

Plate 1674   4-Ball Pendulum
Calendar Clock
USE .0036″ (.091mm) HOROLOVAR
Units 36A, 36B   (19 x 38)

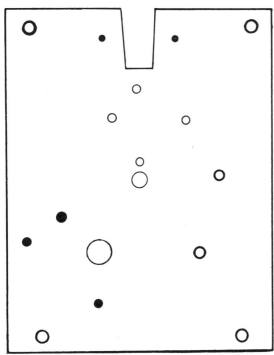

Plate 1677   4-Ball Pendulum
                Pin Pallet Escapement
                    Lantern Pinions
USE .0035″* (.089mm*) HOROLOVAR
                        (20 x 38)

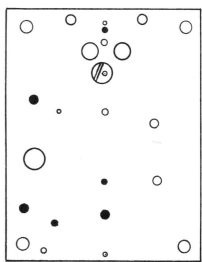

Plate 1678   4-Ball Pendulum
                    Miniature Clock
USE .0025″ (.064mm) HOROLOVAR
Units 28A, 28B   (16 x 36)

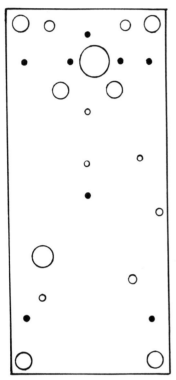

Plate 1681   4-Ball Pendulum
USE .0035″ (.089mm) HOROLOVAR
Unit 31   (19 x 38)

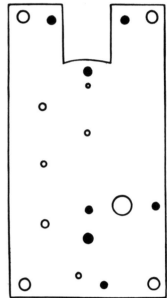

Plate 1682   4-Ball Pendulum
                       Miniature Clock
USE .0032″ (.081mm) HOROLOVAR
Unit 14A
USE .003″ (.076mm) HOROLOVAR
Unit 14B   (13 x 32)

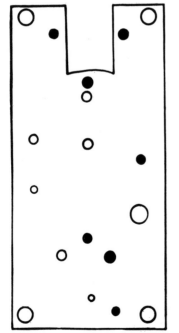

Plate 1683   4-Ball Pendulum
USE .0035″ (.089mm) HOROLOVAR
Units 13A, 13B   (20 x 38)

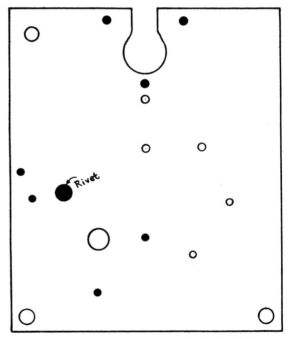

Rivet

Plate 1685   4-Ball Pendulum
USE .0038″ (.097mm) HOROLOVAR
Unit 33   (19 x 38)

142

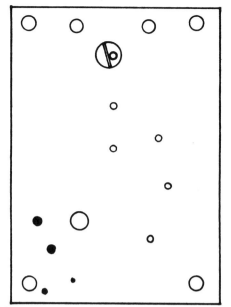

Plate 1689   Disc Pendulum
Miniature Clock
USE .0025″ (.064mm) HOROLOVAR

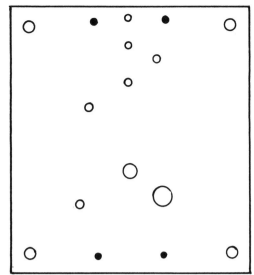

Plate 1691   3-Ball Pendulum
Pin Pallet Escapement
USE .0036″ (.091mm) HOROLOVAR
Unit 40

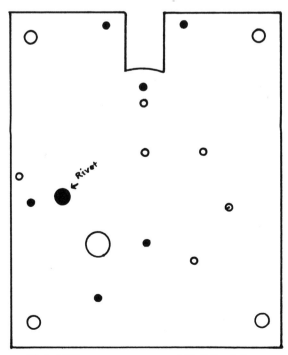

Plate 1693   4-Ball Pendulum
USE .0038″ (.097mm) HOROLOVAR
Unit 33   (19 x 38)

Plate 1701   4-Ball Pendulum
                                   Battery Clock
USE .0022″ (.053mm) HOROLOVAR
Unit 47

SECTION 5 . . . SUSPENSION SPRING UNITS

This section contains accurate illustrations of the manufacturers' pendulum suspension spring units for practically all clocks imported into the U. S. from 1949 until the time of publication of this Guide. It does not include suspension units from older clocks, because no original manufacturers' samples are available, and because it is almost impossible to tell whether or not units in the old clocks available have been altered at one time or another.

The important contribution which these illustrations offer to the repairman is that, since they have been reproduced in exact size, they make it possible for him, when replacing a suspension spring, to cut it to the correct length and also set the fork in the correct position on the spring. A quick examination of the illustrations will show that the distance between top block and fork varies considerably from clock to clock. A variation of more than one sixteenth of an inch in the correct position of the fork on the spring may mean the difference between a correct adjustment and one which will give all kinds of trouble.

The position of the fork on the suspension spring is directly related to the operation of the escapement. A fork, if set too low, will cause the anchor to flutter; if set too high, it will cause a jerky motion of the anchor which ultimately may cause the clock to stop. Either of these two poor escapement actions, caused only by an improper position of the fork on the suspension spring, is often thought to be the result of an incorrectly adjusted escapement. It will be worth while, therefore, to check the correct unit in this section with the one in the clock you are repairing, particularly before coming to the conclusion that your problem is in the escapement.

1 - KUNDO STANDARD 49 - USE .0032" (.081mm) HOROLOVAR

   Fits all clocks from the first model, made well over fifty years ago, until about 1952. Bottom suspension block locking lever (29) was replaced with improved locking lever (28) in models made after World War I.

2 - KUNDO STANDARD 52 - USE .0032" (.081mm) HOROLOVAR

   Used with only a few thousand clocks in 1953. A special stirrup-type bottom block (11) was designed to be used with improved locking lever (30), but required the use of a special pendulum hook (17). There are no screws in the top or bottom blocks; the suspension spring is "pinched" tight. No replacement Units of this type are available. Replacement must be made with Unit 3A. However, it is also necessary to replace pendulum hook (17) with type (16).

3A- KUNDO STANDARD 53 - USE .0032" (.081mm) HOROLOVAR

   Has fixed pin through the bottom block (12) and was designed to be used with improved locking lever (30). Unit 3A is interchangeable with Unit 1 and may be used in clocks with locking levers (29) and (28).

3B- KUNDO STANDARD 54 - USE .0032" (.081mm) HOROLOVAR

   Used with the first locking pendulum model. It is exactly the same as Unit 3A except that there is no fixed pin through the bottom block (13). Instead, a cotter pin (14) holds the bottom block (13) in "hook" (18) or (19), the latter having a larger threaded hole to fit the improved, stronger pendulum center rod. Note that Suspension Unit 3B with pendulum locking mechanism is identified by pendulum locking lever (31) which is *ABOVE* the movement platform (32).

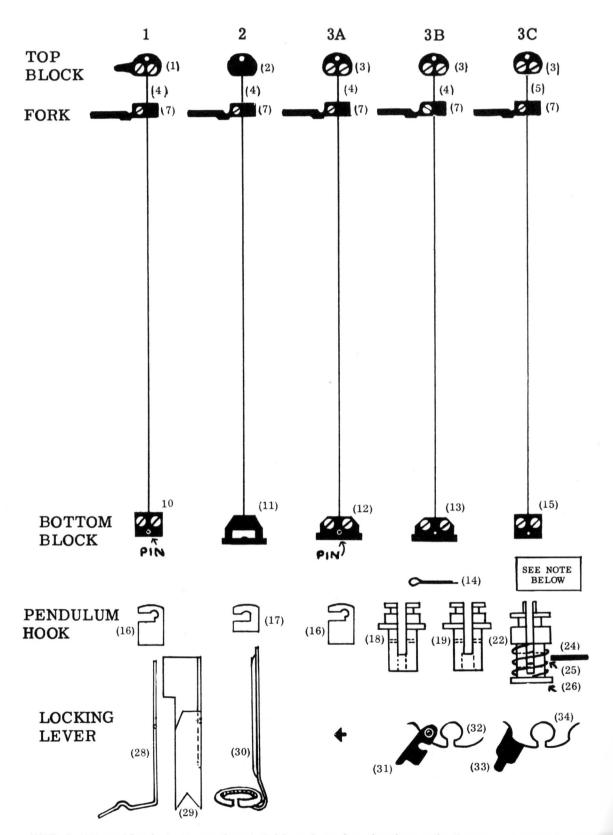

NOTE: In 1958, pendulum hook (22) was changed slightly in design from that shown in the illustration. However the collar spring and pin perform the same functions.

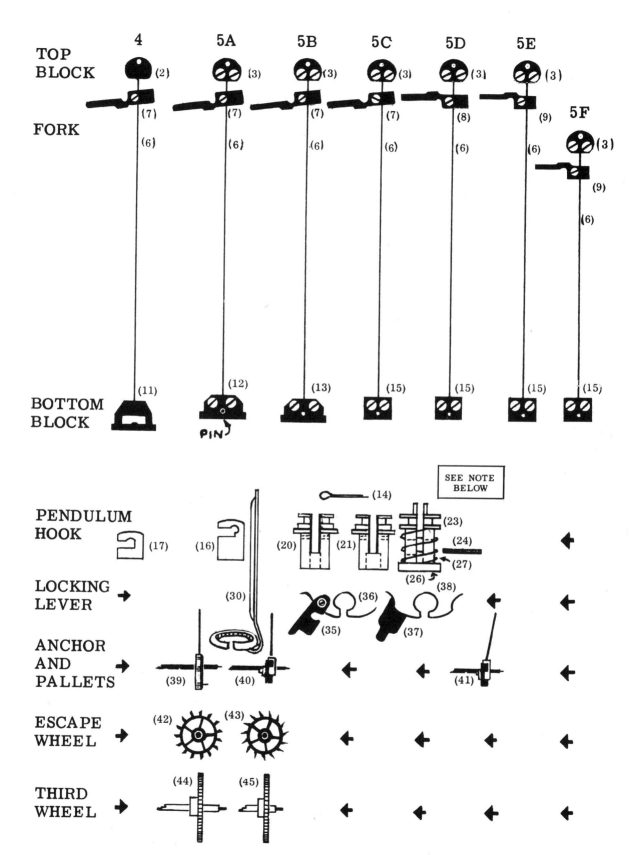

	4	5A	5B	5C	5D	5E	5F

TOP BLOCK (2) (3) (3) (3) (3) (3) (3)

FORK (7) (7) (7) (7) (8) (9) (9)

(6) (6) (6) (6) (6) (6) (6)

BOTTOM BLOCK (11) (12) (13) (15) (15) (15) (15)

PIN

SEE NOTE BELOW

(14)

PENDULUM HOOK (17) (16) (20) (21) (23) (24) (27) (26)

LOCKING LEVER → (30) (35) (36) (37) (38)

ANCHOR AND PALLETS → (39) (40) ← ← (41) ←

ESCAPE WHEEL → (42) (43) ← ← ← ←

THIRD WHEEL → (44) (45) ← ← ← ←

NOTE: In 1958, pendulum hook (26) was changed slightly in design from that shown in the illustration. However the collar, spring and pin perform the same functions.

147

3C - KUNDO STANDARD 55 - USE .0032" (.081mm) HOROLOVAR

Used with the latest type locking pendulum model, in production since 1954. It is identified by pendulum locking lever (33) which is *BELOW* the movement platform (34). A loose brass pin (24), 10 millimeters long, holds the bottom suspension block (15) in the pendulum "hook" (22), and is kept in place by a collar (26) which, with pressure from coil spring (25), locks the ends of the pin. In order to detach the pendulum, the collar must be raised against the coil spring until an end of the pin is exposed and the pin then withdrawn.

4 - KUNDO JUNIOR 52 - USE .0023" (.058mm) HOROLOVAR

Used in only a few thousand clocks in 1953. A special stirrup-type bottom block (11) was designed to be used with improved locking lever (30), but required the use of a special pendulum hook (17). There are no screws in the top or bottom blocks; the suspension spring is "pinched" tight. No replacement Units of this type are available. Replacement must be made with Unit 5A. However, it is also necessary to replace pendulum hook (17) with type (16). Unit 4 was used only with movements having pin pallet escapement.

5A - KUNDO JUNIOR 53 - USE .0023" (.058mm) HOROLOVAR

Has fixed pin through the bottom block (12). It was used with both the 1953 model (with pin pallet escapement) and the 1954 model (with "Graham" escapement).

NOTE: Kundo Junior movements with "pin pallet" escapement can be converted to "Graham" (dead beat) escapement. Interchange three parts: Substitute Anchor (40), Escape Wheel (43), and Third Wheel (45), for corresponding parts (39), (42) and (44). The Third Wheel substitution is necessary because the position of the old wheel on the arbor is such that it would make it interfere with the new Escape Wheel. (Also see NOTE under Unit 5E)

5B - KUNDO JUNIOR 54 - USE .0023" (.058mm) HOROLOVAR

Used with the first locking pendulum model. It is exactly the same as Unit 5A except that there is no pin through bottom block (13). Instead, a cotter pin (14) holds the bottom block (13) in "hook" (20) or (21), the latter having a larger threaded hole to fit the improved, stronger pendulum center rod. Note that Suspension Unit 5B with pendulum locking mechanism is identified by pendulum locking lever (35) which is *ABOVE* the movement platform (36). (See NOTE under Unit 5E)

5C - KUNDO JUNIOR 55 - USE .0023" (.058mm) HOROLOVAR

First of three Units used with the latest type of locking pendulum, identified by pendulum locking lever (37) which is *BELOW* the movement platform (38). A loose brass pin (24), 10 millimeters long, holds the suspension block (15) in the pendulum "hook" (23), and is kept in place by a collar (26) which, with pressure from coil spring (27), locks the ends of the pin. In order to detach the pendulum, the collar must be raised against the coil spring until an end of the pin is exposed and the pin then withdrawn. Units 5C, 5D and 5E are interchangeable. Unit 5E is recommended.

5D - KUNDO JUNIOR 55 - USE .0023" (.058mm) HOROLOVAR

Second of the three Units used with the latest locking pendulum model. Note that fork (8) is in an inverted position. The screw in some forks (8) enters from the opposite side to the one illustrated. Units 5D, 5C and 5E are interchangeable. Unit 5E is recommended.

5E - KUNDO JUNIOR 56 - USE .0023" (.058mm) HOROLOVAR

Third and latest of the three Units used with the latest locking pendulum model. The only change is in fork (9) which is lighter in weight than forks (7) and (8). Functionally, there is no advantage in using Unit 5E in place of 5D. They are both interchangeable. However, Kundo has found that the lighter fork is less likely to bend the suspension spring, between the top block and fork, during severe transportation shocks. Latest design of fork (9) is made with a closed end which not only prevents the anchor pin from slipping out, but also helps to keep the tines from becoming bent. Units 5E, 5C and 5D are interchangeable. Unit 5E is recommended.

All movements using Unit 5E have straight, upright anchor pins. If the pin is bent offset to the rear, use Unit 5F.

NOTE: If a clock with Units 5A, 5B, 5C, 5D or 5E does not produce good pendulum motion (320 to 450 degrees), note the position of the Anchor, Escape Wheel and Third Wheel. If they are

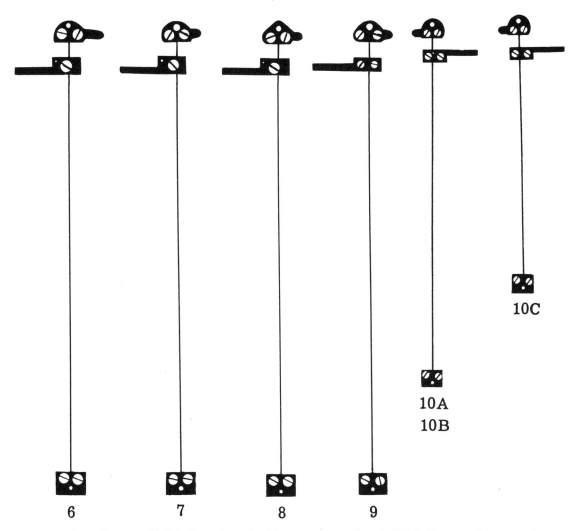

| 6 | 7 | 8 | 9 | 10A 10B | 10C |

arranged as shown in "A," below, they should be rearranged as in "B." Best pendulum motion is obtained when the anchor pin is as near to the back plate as possible.

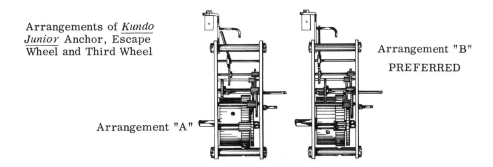

Arrangements of *Kundo Junior* Anchor, Escape Wheel and Third Wheel

Arrangement "B"
PREFERRED

Arrangement "A"

5F - KUNDO MIDGET 57 - USE .0022" (.056mm) HOROLOVAR

Regulating limits of the pendulum for this model are critical and the correct Horolovar spring strength should be slightly weaker than .0022" (.056mm). If .0022" (.056mm) is found to be too heavy, you can easily thin it. Hold the pendulum firmly, while it is attached to the spring. Rub a small, folded piece of fine emery cloth up and down the spring, keeping it taut. A very few strokes should do the trick.

All movements using the 5F Unit have anchor pins with offset bends to the rear. The pin is so designed to make contact with the suspension fork slightly *behind* the back plate.

6 - SCHATZ STANDARD 49 USE .004" (.102mm) HOROLOVAR

This is the original Unit used with the 1949 model clock. Units 6, 7, 8 and 9 are interchangeable.

7 - SCHATZ STANDARD 52 - USE .004" (.102mm) HOROLOVAR

Second Unit used with the 1949 model clock. The only change is in the shape of the top block. Units 6, 7, 8, and 9 are interchangeable.

8 - SCHATZ STANDARD 53 - USE .004" (.102mm) HOROLOVAR

Third Unit used with the 1949 model clock. Again, the only change is in the shape of the top block. Units 6, 7, 8, and 9 are interchangeable.

9 - SCHATZ STANDARD 54 - USE .004" (.102mm) HOROLOVAR

This Unit was first used with the model 1954 clock. A change was made in the design of the fork and in the position of the fork on the suspension spring. However, Units 6, 7, 8, and 9 are interchangeable.

10A - SCHATZ MINIATURE 53 - USE .0023" (.058mm) HOROLOVAR

This unit is used with the glass- or plastic-domed clock; also with the "London Coach" and "Bermuda" models.

10B - SCHATZ 1000-DAY 54 - USE .0024" (.061mm) HOROLOVAR

This Unit should be used for all Schatz 1000-Day Clocks.

10C - SCHATZ MIDGET 57 - USE .0022" (.056mm) HOROLOVAR

11A - KERN STANDARD 50 - USE .0036" (.091mm) HOROLOVAR

This Unit should be used only with models having detachable pendulum.

11B - KERN STANDARD 54 - USE .0036" (.091mm) HOROLOVAR

This Unit should be used only with models equipped with locking pendulum mechanisms. It is slightly longer than Unit 11A.

12A - KERN MINIATURE 54 - USE .002" (.051mm) HOROLOVAR

Note that the fork tines are supposed to be bent slightly upward as illustrated. Units 12A, 12B, and 12C are interchangeable. Unit 12C is recommended.

12B - KERN MINIATURE 56 - USE .002" (.051mm) HOROLOVAR

The fork in this Unit is preferred to the one illustrated in 12A, because it is lighter in weight. Units 12A, 12B, and 12C are interchangeable. Unit 12C is recommended.

12C - KERN MINIATURE 57 - USE .002" (.051mm) HOROLOVAR

The top block of this Unit is preferred to the one used in 12A and 12B, because it will hold the spring tighter. Units 12A, 12B, and 12C are interchangeable. Unit 12C is preferred.

12D - KERN MINIATURE 58 - USE .0019" (.048mm) HOROLOVAR

In addition to the lighter spring strength, this Unit is approximately 2 millimeters shorter than Units 12A, 12B, and 12C.

12E - KERN MIDGET 58 - USE .002" (.051mm) HOROLOVAR

Regulating limits of the pendulum for this model are critical and the correct Horolovar spring strength should be slightly weaker than .002" (.051mm). If .002" (.051mm) is found to be too heavy, you can easily thin it. Hold the pendulum firmly, while it is attached to the spring. Rub a small, folded piece of fine emery cloth up and down the spring, keeping it taut. A very few strokes should do the trick.

12F - KERN MINIATURE 61 - USE .0023" (.058mm) HOROLOVAR

This unit is used with the only Kern movement which has the mainspring barrel on the right side, when viewed from the back. With few exceptions, this movement is used only in a model covered with a brass and plastic-sided case.

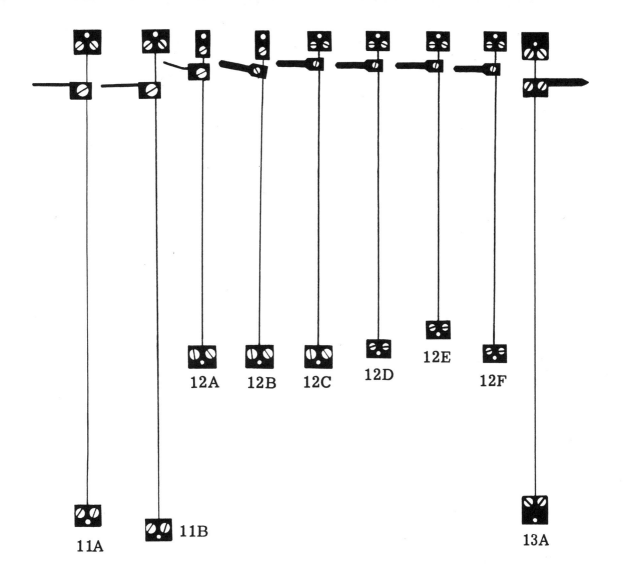

12A 12B 12C 12D

12E

12F

11A

11B

13A

13A – KOMA STANDARD 50 – USE .0035" (.089mm) HOROLOVAR
    This is the original Unit used with the 1950 model. Subsequently, the shape of the top and bottom suspension blocks were changed as shown in Unit 13B. Units 13A and 13B are interchangeable.

13B – KOMA STANDARD 52 – USE .0035" (.089mm) HOROLOVAR
    Second Unit used with the Koma Standard model. Units 13A and 13B are interchangeable.

13C – KOMA STANDARD 56 – USE .0035" (.089mm) HOROLOVAR
    This unit should be used only with models equipped with locking pendulum mechanisms. It is slightly shorter than Units 13A and 13B.

14A – KOMA MINIATURE 54 – USE .0032" (.081mm) HOROLOVAR
    This Unit is used with two different model clocks -- one with a pendulum having a slightly longer axis than the other. Whereas the Units are interchangeable with both model clocks, the model having the longer pendulum axis also has slightly higher pillars which raise the movement.

14B – KOMA MINIATURE 65 – USE .003" (.076mm) HOROLOVAR
    Models requiring this unit have one distinctive feature:
        The pendulum weights are shaped like this . . . .

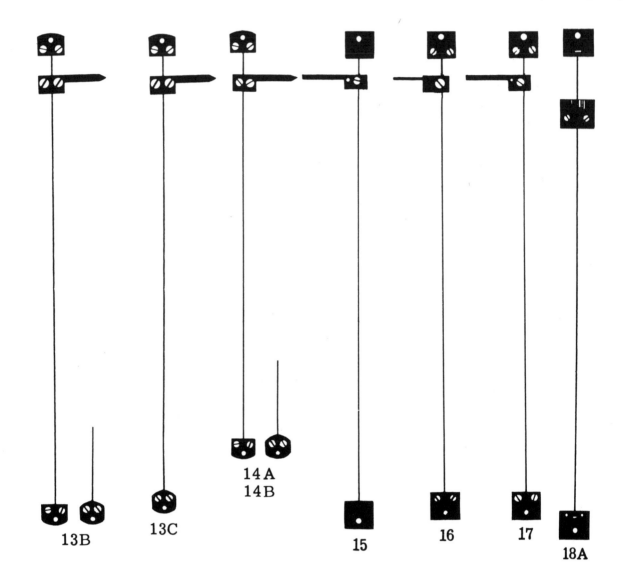

13B   13C   14A 14B   15   16   17   18A

15 - LINK STANDARD 52 - USE .0037" (.094mm) HOROLOVAR

First Unit used with the Link Standard clock, there are no screws in the top and bottom blocks. The suspension spring is "pinched" tight. No replacement units of this type are available. Replacement must be made with Unit 16 or 17. Units 15, 16 and 17 are interchangeable. Unit 16 is recommended.

16 - LINK STANDARD 52 - USE .0037" (.094mm) HOROLOVAR

The only difference between Units 16 and 17 is in the shape of the forks. Units 16 and 17 are interchangeable. Unit 16 is recommended.

17 - LINK STANDARD 53 - USE .0037" (.094mm) HOROLOVAR

The only difference between Units 17 and 16 is in the shape of the forks. Units 17 and 16 are interchangeable. Unit 16 is recommended.

18A - PETERSEN STANDARD 53 - USE .0033" (.084mm) HOROLOVAR

First Unit used with the Petersen Standard clock, there are no screws in the top and bottom blocks. The suspension spring is "pinched" tight. No replacement Units of this type are available. Replacement must be made with Units 18B or 18C. Units 18A, 18B and 18C are interchangeable. Unit 18C is recommended.

152

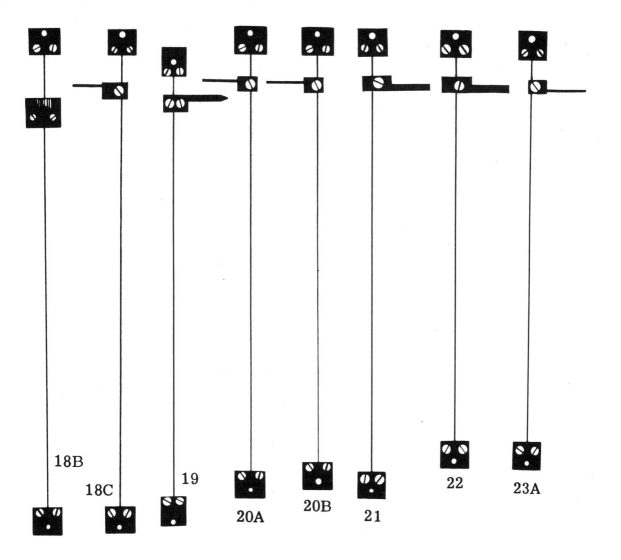

18B

18C

19

20A

20B

21

22

23A

18B - PETERSEN STANDARD 54 - USE .0033" (.084mm) HOROLOVAR

The only difference between Units 18B and 18C is in the shape of the fork. The design of the Petersen fork, in Units 18B (and 18A), makes it necessary to set the suspension saddle position 90° from that normal to all other clocks. Since there is no functional reason for this different design, if a Petersen fork is not available, use Unit 18C. Units 18B, 18C (and 18A) are interchangeable.

18C - PETERSEN STANDARD 54 (Alternate) - USE .0033" (.084mm) HOROLOVAR

This Unit is functionally the same as Unit 18B (and 18A), but it is provided with a conventional type fork. Units 18C, 18B (and 18A) are interchangeable.

19 - HERR STANDARD 53 - USE .0035" (.089mm) HOROLOVAR

This Unit was used only with the 1953 model. The movement is standard size, but with narrow plates. (Sometimes thin brass "wings" were added to make the plates look wider). From the shape of the blocks and fork, it would appear as though Herr temporarily used those manufactured by Koma. (Note similarity with Unit 13A). Units 19, 20A and 21 are interchangeable. Unit 20A is recommended.

20A - HERR STANDARD 54 - USE .0035" (.089mm) HOROLOVAR

The only difference between Unit 20A and 19 is in the shape of the blocks and fork. It differs from Unit 21 only in the shape and position of the fork on the suspension spring. Units 20A, 19 and 21 are interchangeable. Unit 20A is recommended.

153

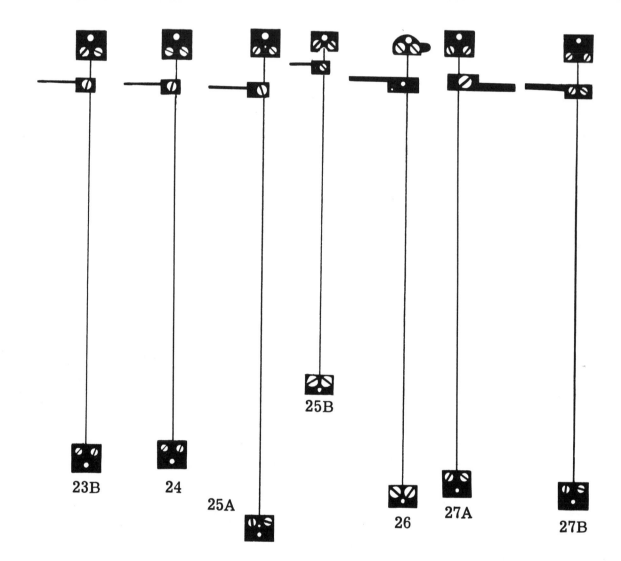

23B   24

25A

25B

26   27A

27B

20B - HERR STANDARD 54 (Square case) - USE .0033" (.084mm) HOROLOVAR

This Unit is used with the Herr "Atlantis" -- a Standard, narrow plate movement in a square case with glass sides, mirror back, and a handle on top.

21 - HERR STANDARD 53 - USE .0035" (.089mm) HOROLOVAR

This Unit differs from Unit 20A only in the shape and position of the fork on the suspension spring. Units 21, 19 and 20A are interchangeable. Unit 20A is recommended.

22 - REINER STANDARD 53 (Miniature Movement) - USE .003" (.076mm) HOROLOVAR

See details about the clocks using this Unit under Unit 23A. Units 22, 23A and 24 are interchangeable. Unit 23A is recommended.

23A - REINER STANDARD 53 (Miniature Movement) - USE .003" (.076mm) HOROLOVAR

This Unit is used with the Standard size clock with miniature movement. Most of these clocks are under the Standard 5 1/2" x 10 1/2" glass dome, but another model, known as the "Venita," has a glass sided "hood," with a curved top, which fits over a flat base. This miniature movement, which is also made by Herr, is their first model, identified as such by the fact that the anchor arbor pivot hole, in the back plate, is *below* the top suspension guard holding screw. Units 23A, 22 and 24 are interchangeable, the only difference being in the shape of the fork or in its position on the suspension spring. The alternate positions of the fork do not affect the functioning of the escapement. Unit 23A is recommended. For the miniature clock (under a 4 5/8" x 8" glass dome) with this movement, use Units 28A or 28B.

154

23B - REINER STANDARD 56 (Miniature Movement) - USE .0032" (.081mm) HOROLOVAR

This Unit should be used with the improved movement (larger escape wheel and anchor) in the clocks described above for Unit 23A. This movement (which is also made by Herr) is identified by the fact that the anchor arbor pivot hole, in the back plate, is *above* the top suspension guard holding screw. When this change in the movement was made, the weight of the pendulum, for some unknown reason, was increased. Thus it is necessary to use the slightly heavier .0032" (.081mm) HOROLOVAR suspension spring. For the miniature clock (under a 4 5/8" x 8" glass dome) with this movement, use Unit 28C.

24 - REINER STANDARD 53 (Miniature Movement) - USE .003" (.076mm) HOROLOVAR

See details about the clocks using this Unit under Unit 23A. Units 24, 22 and 23A are interchangeable. Unit 23A is recommended.

25A - HERMLE STANDARD 53 - USE .0033" (.084mm) HOROLOVAR

25B - HERMLE MINIATURE 54 - USE .0022" (.056mm) HOROLOVAR

It is necessary for the top suspension block to be cut out as indicated in order for the spring to be of the correct length above the fork, and for the fork to contact the anchor pin at the proper point. If a Hermle block is not available, a square block can be filed to this shape.

26 - WURTHNER STANDARD 53 - USE .004" (.102mm) HOROLOVAR

27A - HERR STANDARD 53 - USE .004" (.102mm) HOROLOVAR

This Unit is used with all Herr Standard clocks having wide plate movements.

27B - HERR STANDARD 55 - USE .0038" (.097mm) HOROLOVAR

This Unit is from one of several clocks with pendulum regulating nuts threaded in the opposite direction from most others. To make the pendulum go faster, you must turn the nut *clockwise.*

27C - NEUECK 57 - USE .0036" (.091mm) HOROLOVAR

The trade mark WILMAC or NEUECK appears on the back plates of most of these clocks.

28A - HERR MINIATURE 53 - USE .0025" (.064mm) HOROLOVAR

This Unit differs from Unit 28B only in the size of its top and bottom blocks. The blocks measure 6.0mm x 7.0mm and are smaller than those used for 28B.

28B - HERR MINIATURE 54 - USE .0025" (.064mm) HOROLOVAR

This Unit differs from Unit 28A only in the size of its top and bottom blocks. The blocks measure 7.5mm x 8.5mm and are larger than those used for 28A. Units 28A and 28B are used in the first model miniature Herr clock, identified as such by the fact that the anchor arbor pivot hole in the back plate is *below* the top suspension guard holding screw. If the pivot hole is *above* the screw, use Unit 28C.

28C - HERR MINIATURE 56 - USE .0028" (.071mm) HOROLOVAR

This Unit is used with the latest model miniature Herr clock. It is distinguished from the first model by the fact that the anchor arbor pivot hole in the back plate is *above* the top suspension guard holding screw. If the pivot hole is *below* the screw, use Unit 28A or 28B. This Unit is from one of several recently manufactured clocks with pendulum regulating nuts threaded in the opposite direction from most others. To make the pendulum go faster, you must turn the nut *clockwise.* This unit also fits the model in the six-sided case.

29A - HENN MINIATURE 52 - USE .0023" (.058mm) HOROLOVAR

The only difference between Unit 29A and 29B is in the smaller diameter of the hole in the top block. The top block holding screw for Unit 29A is 1.4mm in diameter.

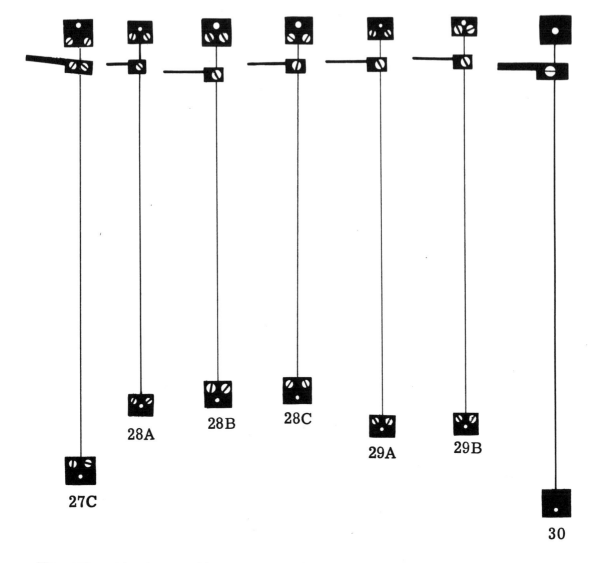

27C 28A 28B 28C 29A 29B 30

29B - HENN MINIATURE 53 - USE .0023" (.058mm) HOROLOVAR

The only difference between Unit 29B and 29A is in the larger diameter of the hole in the top block. The top block holding screw for 29B is 1.9mm in diameter. Some of the recently manufactured pendulums for this clock were made with regulating nuts threaded in the opposite direction from most others. To make these pendulums go faster, you must turn the nut *clockwise*.

30 - HENN STANDARD 51 - USE .0035" (.089mm) HOROLOVAR

Used with the first (wide plate) movement, there are no screws in the top and bottom blocks. The suspension spring is "pinched" tight. No replacement Units of this type are available. Replacement must be made with Unit 31. Units 30 and 31 are interchangeable.

31 - HENN STANDARD 52 - USE .0035" (.089mm) HOROLOVAR

Second Unit used with the wide plate movement. Units 31 and 30 are interchangeable. Unit 31 is recommended.

32 - HENN STANDARD 54 - USE .0037" (.094mm) HOROLOVAR

Used with the narrow plate movement. The clock is equipped with locking pendulum.

33 - JAUCH & HALLER 54 - USE .0038" (.097mm) HOROLOVAR

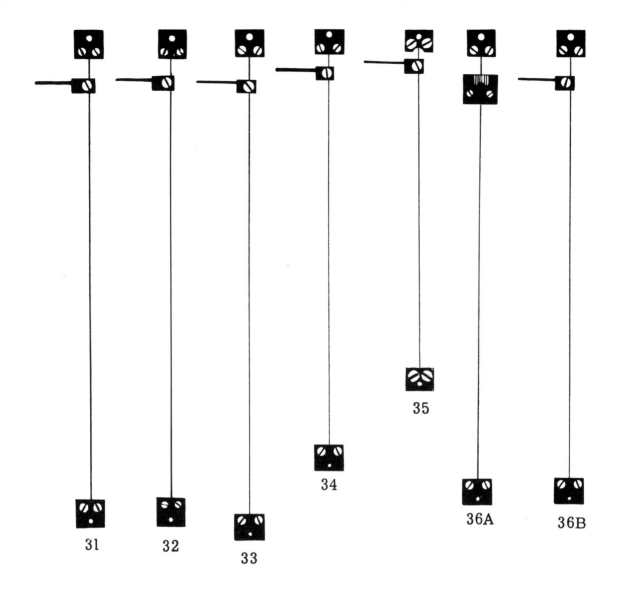

31   32

33

34

35

36A   36B

34 - KAISER STANDARD 54 - USE .003" (.076mm) HOROLOVAR

This Unit is used with the model having the globe (world) pendulum.

35 - LINK MINIATURE 56 - USE .0021" (.053mm) HOROLOVAR

It is necessary for the top suspension block to be cut out as indicated in order for the spring to be of the correct length above the fork, and for the fork to contact the anchor pin at the proper point. If a Link block is not available, a square block can be filed to this shape.

36A - PETERSEN STANDARD 55 (Calendar) - USE .0036" (.091mm) HOROLOVAR

The only difference between Units 36A and 36B is in the shape of the fork. The design of the Petersen fork in 36A makes it necessary to set the suspension saddle position 90° from that normal to all other clocks. Since there is no functional reason for this different design, if a Petersen fork is not available, Unit 36B is recommended.

36B - PETERSEN STANDARD 55 (Alternate) - USE .0036" (.091mm) HOROLOVAR

This Unit is functionally the same as Unit 36A, but it is provided with a conventional type fork. Units 36B and 36A are interchangeable. Unit 36B is recommended.

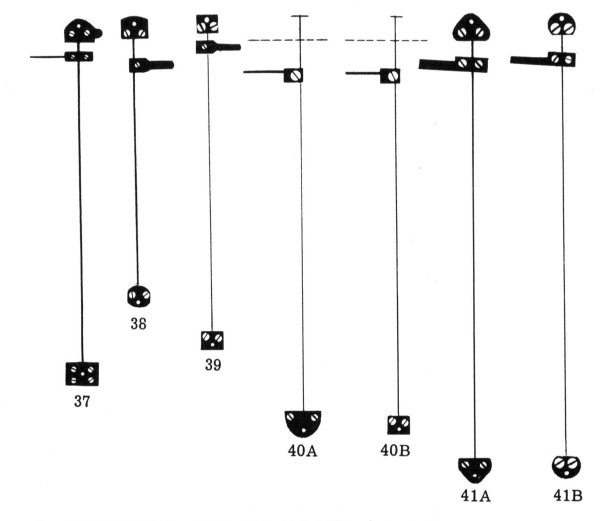

37 - WURTHNER MIDGET 57 - USE .002" (.051mm) HOROLOVAR
   Only a very small number of these clocks were produced.

38 - KOMA MIDGET 57 - USE .0022" (.056mm) HOROLOVAR

39 - SIEGFRIED HALLER 57 - USE .0019" (.048mm) HOROLOVAR
   Only a very small number of these clocks were produced.

40A - CRESCENT STANDARD 55 - USE .0036" (.091mm) HOROLOVAR
   This clock was manufactured in Japan by Ishikara Clock Co., Ltd. The suspension saddle is designed to hold the top of the suspension spring like a vise, so there is no top suspension block for this Unit. The dotted line indicates the location of the bottom of the saddle.

   Units 40A and 40B are interchangeable. Unit 40B is recommended.

40B - CRESCENT STANDARD 55 - USE .0036" (.091mm) HOROLOVAR
   Parts for this Unit are more easily available than they are for Unit 40A. Units 40A and 40B are interchangeable. Unit 40B is recommended.

41A - MASTER STANDARD 55 - USE .0035" (.089mm) HOROLOVAR
   This clock was manufactured in Japan by Nisshin Clock Industrial Co., Ltd. Units 41A and 41B are interchangeable. Unit 41B is recommended.

41B - MASTER STANDARD 55 - USE .0035" (.089mm) HOROLOVAR
   Parts for this Unit are more easily available than they are for Unit 41A. Units 41A and 41B are interchangeable. Unit 41B is recommended.

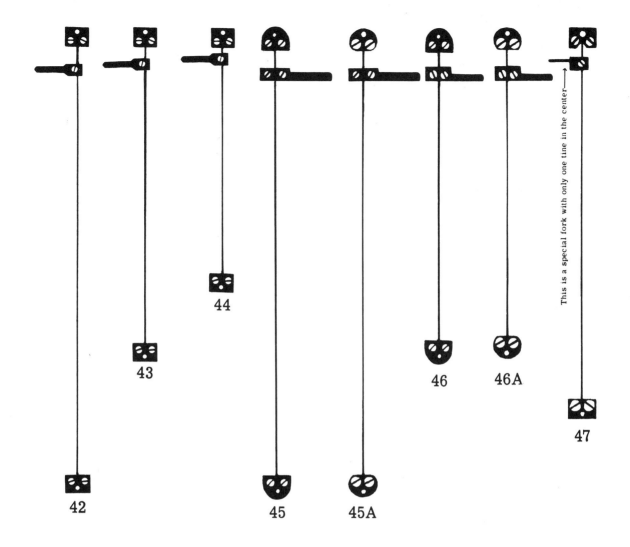

This is a special fork with only one tine in the center→

42 - S. HALLER STANDARD 70 - USE .0028" (.071mm) HOROLOVAR

43 - S. HALLER MINIATURE 70 - USE .0022" (.056mm) HOROLOVAR

44 - S. HALLER MIDGET 70 - USE .0018" (.056mm) HOROLOVAR

45 - MASTER STANDARD 70 - USE .0034" (.086mm) HOROLOVAR
The plates of this movement have rounded corners. The plates of the movement that uses Unit 41A or 41B have square corners - see Plate 1416A.

45A - MASTER STANDARD 70 - USE .0034" (.086mm) HOROLOVAR
This Unit is interchangeable with Unit 45

46 - NEW MASTER 100-DAY - USE .0028" (.071mm) HOROLOVAR

46A - NEW MASTER 100-DAY - USE .0028" (.071mm) HOROLOVAR
This Unit is interchangeable with Unit 46

47 - HERMLE 71 (Battery operated) - USE .0022" (.053mm) HOROLOVAR
The strength of the suspension spring in this Unit is not critical, because the pendulum does not regulate the clock's timekeeping. The movement gives independent impulses to the pendulum which keeps it oscillating for appearance only.

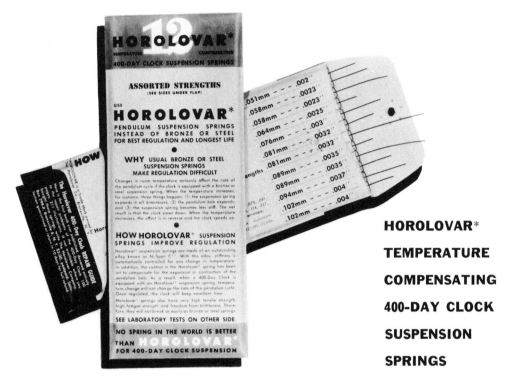

HOROLOVAR*

TEMPERATURE

COMPENSATING

400-DAY CLOCK

SUSPENSION

SPRINGS

A HOROLOVAR SPRING FOR EVERY 400-DAY CLOCK
TWENTY-FOUR STRENGTHS AVAILABLE

INCHES		MILLIMETERS

Packaged Dozens—(Single Strength)

.0018	.0019	.002	.0021	.0022	.0023	.046	.048	.051	.053	.056	.058
.0024	.0025	.0027	.0028	.003	.0031	.061	.064	.069	.071	.076	.079
.0032	.0033	.0034	.0035	.0036	.0037	.081	.084	.086	.089	.091	.094
.0038	.004	.0045	.005	.0055	.006	.097	.102	.114	.127	.140	.152

Packaged Dozen—(Popular Assorted Strengths)

.002	.0023	.0023	.0025	.051	.058	.058	.064
.003	.0032	.0032	.0035	.076	.081	.081	.089
.0035	.0037	.004	.004	.089	.094	.102	.102

Packaged Dozen—(Intermediate Strengths)

.0019	.0021	.0022	.0024	.048	.053	.056	.061
.0028	.0031	.0033	.0036	.071	.079	.084	.091
.0038	.0045	.005	.0055	.097	.114	.127	.140

Price $3.00 Per Packaged Dozen
3 for $1.25—Single Strengths 50¢

AT LEADING MATERIAL HOUSES

*Trade Mark Registered, U. S. Patent Office

HOW HOROLOVAR SUSPENSION SPRINGS IMPROVE REGULATION

Horolovar* suspension springs are made of an outstanding alloy known as Ni-Span C**. With this alloy, spring stiffness is automatically controlled for any change in temperature. In addition, the control in the Horolovar* spring has been set to compensate for expansion or contraction of the pendulum bob. As a result, when a 400-Day Clock is equipped with an Horolovar* suspension spring, temperature change will not change the rate of the pendulum cycle. Once regulated, the clock will keep excellent time.

WHY BRONZE OR STEEL SPRINGS MAKE REGULATION DIFFICULT

Changes in room temperature seriously affect the rate of the pendulum cycle if the clock is equipped with a bronze or steel suspension spring. When the temperature increases, for instance, three things happen: (1) the suspension spring expands in all dimensions; (2) the pendulum bob expands; and (3) the suspension spring loses part of its stiffness. The net result is that the clock slows down. When the temperature decreases, the effect is reversed, and the clock speeds up.

HOROLOVAR SUSPENSION SPRINGS WON'T BREAK

Horolovar* springs have very high tensile strength, high fatigue strength and freedom from brittleness. Therefore, they will not break easily as do bronze or steel springs.

HOROLOVAR SUSPENSION SPRINGS ARE USED INTERNATIONALLY

Horolovar springs are used by leading 400-Day Clock manufacturers in Germany and by clock repairmen in England, France, Canada, Hawaii, Puerto Rico, Saudi Arabia, Australia, Etc.

NO SPRING IN THE WORLD IS BETTER THAN HOROLOVAR FOR 400-DAY CLOCK PENDULUM SUSPENSION!

* HOROLOVAR is a Registered Trade Mark owned by The Horolovar Co., Bronxville, N. Y.

** NI SPAN C is a Registered Trade Mark of The International Nickel Co., Inc., made exclusively by H. A. Wilson Co. Dept. of Engelhard Minerals and Chemical Corp.

	HOROLOVAR	STEEL	BRONZE
Time Error Per Day For 5° F. Temperature Change	2 seconds	35 seconds	60 seconds
Tensile Strength Index	100	133	73
Fatigue Strength Index	100	133	50
Brittleness Resistance (Ductility) Index	100	24	67
Corrosion Resistance	Good	Rusts	Good
Magnetic Property	Slight	Strong	None

WHAT CLOCKMAKERS SAY ABOUT HOROLOVAR SUSPENSION SPRINGS

"Best wishes to you for correcting an error that has been in these clocks for 50 years."
M. A. York, CW
Raleigh, N. C.

"Horolovar springs have changed the 400-Day Clock from an ornament to an accurate time piece."
Fred B. Patterson
Tucson, Arizona

"One clock that I used a Horolovar spring on has not varied more than ½ minute in the past five months."
Louis Romaine, CW, CMBHI
Williston Park
Long Island, N. Y.

"We use only Horolovar springs on our repair jobs."
Fred C. Urfer, Jr.
The Clock Shoppe
Miami, Florida

"I have been using Horolovar springs in all of the clocks that I sell and service, because they are so much better than bronze or steel."
M. C. Campbell
Campbell's Clock Shop
Grand Rapids, Mich.

"Saved us hours of labor and time."
James C. Romano
Electric Clock Service
Boston, Mass.

"As soon as we receive new clocks, we remove the springs the clocks are equipped with and replace with Horolovar."
Edward C. Turnbull
Turnbull's
Port Arthur, Texas

"We have repaired about 100 clocks in the past year and find Horolovar springs the best."
J. Seethaler
B. W. Cobb Watch and Clock Shop
Portland, Oregon

"The Horolovar Co. is marketing an assortment of 400-Day Clock suspension springs. They have an ingenious method of packing them. Each size comes in a separate compartment—of all things, a soda straw. Glued into an envelope, they make an ideal package. These springs are made from a nickel-steel alloy and are not as sensitive to temperature as the bronze spring. We've found that they handle much better than bronze, too. The Assorted Dozen package contains ten different strengths. One may begin in the middle—that is, put on the .004"; if it is too strong, remove it and use the next weaker spring—or if it is too stiff go the other way. That is what we meant by 'handle better.' We've found that Horolovar springs don't bend, kink, etc., from these 'trys' as did the bronze."
J. E. Coleman
Clockwise and Otherwise
The American Horologist and Jeweler

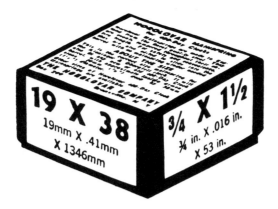

HOROLOVAR* 400-DAY CLOCK MAINSPRINGS
(Made in England)

AVAILABLE FOR EVERY MODEL

	Width of Spring		Inside Diameter of Barrel	Length	Thick-ness		Width of Spring		Inside Diameter of Barrel	Length	Thick-ness
M/M	12	X	24	584	.38	M/M	14	X	30	815	.36
in.	1/2	X	1	23	.015	in.	9/16	X	1-3/16	32	.014
M/M	12	X	25	697	.33	M/M	16	X	36	1039	.46
in.	1/2	X	1	27	.013	in.	5/8	X	1-7/16	41	.018
M/M	12	X	32	1232	.30	M/M	18	X	38	1118	.46
in.	1/2	X	1-1/4	48	.012	in.	11/16	X	1-1/2	44	.018
M/M	13	X	30	972	.36	M/M	19	X	32	951	.41
in.	17/32	X	1-3/16	38	.014	in.	3/4	X	1-1/4	38	.016
M/M	13	X	32	714	.55	M/M	19	X	36	1143	.43
in.	17/32	X	1-1/4	28	.022	in.	3/4	X	1-7/16	45	.017
M/M	14	X	25	697	.33	M/M	19	X	38	1346	.41
in.	9/16	X	1	27	.013	in.	3/4	X	1-1/2	53	.016
M/M	14	X	28	720	.41	M/M	20	X	38	1346	.41
in.	9/16	X	1-1/8	28	.016	in.	25/32	X	1-1/2	53	.016

	Width of Spring		Inside Diameter of Barrel	Length	Thick-ness
M/M	21	X	50	2540	.38
in.	13/16	X	1-15/16	100	.015

HERE'S WHY YOU WILL PREFER
HOROLOVAR 400-DAY CLOCK MAINSPRINGS

SAFE

Horolovar 400-Day Clock mainsprings are made in England of the finest grade Swedish steel, tempered evenly throughout their entire length.

NO MAINSPRING WINDER NEEDED

Each mainspring is coiled to a diameter small enough to slide into the barrel easily. No need to risk distortion by inserting it in the barrel by hand. Saves time.

CORRECTLY SIZED

The box label clearly shows the size of each mainspring. All dimensions are shown both in millimeters and in inches.

WON'T RUST

Coated with a harmless preservative, wrappe a moisture-proof bag, and individually packa, in a convenient box, each mainspring is protect three ways against rust.

Note: When ordering, it is necessary to specify only the width of the spring and the inside diameter of the barrel, i.e. 12 x 25, 19 x 38, etc.

Price $1.50 Each

AT LEADING MATERIAL HOUSES

*Trade Mark Registered, U. S. Patent Office

HOROLOVAR* SUSPENSION SPRING JIGS

FOR ACCURATE ASSEMBLY OF PENDULUM SUSPENSION UNITS

Jig No.	Available for	Jig No.	Available for	Jig No.	Available for
1	Kundo Standard 49 Unit No. 1	5A5B	Kundo Junior 53 and 54 Units No. 5A and 5B	6789	Schatz Standard 49 Units No. 6, 7, 8 and 9
3A3B	Kundo Standard 53 and 54 Units No. 3A and 3B	5E	Kundo Junior 56 Unit No. 5E	10A10B	Schatz Miniature 53 Schatz 1000-Day 54 Units No. 10A and 10B
3C	Kundo Standard 55 Unit No. 3C	5F	Kundo Midget 58 Unit No. 5F	10C	Schatz Midget 57 Unit No. 10C

- Assures accurate location of suspension blocks and fork
- Leaves complete unit in better than factory condition
- Shows correct Horolovar spring strength
- Assures correct length
- Factory tightened screws can be loosened without danger of chewing screw slot
- Screws can be tightened without danger of bending suspension spring

Price $3.75 Each

HOROLOVAR* 400-DAY CLOCK BEAT-SETTING TOOL (Patent Pending)

With this tool, the final and most important operation in 400-Day Clock repair—putting the pendulum in beat—becomes simple, quick, accurate, and permanent! Moreover, it can be used on any model 400-Day Clock suspension saddle, old or new.

This precision tool—expressly designed to make the day-by-day life of the clock repairman easier and more profitable—is the result of 10 years of study and experimentation with many different shapes and sizes of suspension saddles.

HOW TO USE IT IT'S SIMPLE! Just follow these easy steps:

1 Tighten saddle locking screw **first**—not last.

2 Clamp tool tightly on suspension saddle at the place it fits best.

3 Put pendulum in beat.

4 Loosen clamp and remove tool.

IT'S QUICK! The tool saves time usually wasted by frequent over-adjustments and under-adjustments with poor fitting pliers. It remains firmly attached to the saddle during beat-setting operation, thereby making it easier to watch escapement action and pendulum rotation.

IT'S ACCURATE! Its long arm gives you greater control, makes micrometer adjustments possible. Adjustments are smooth—not jerky.

IT'S PERMANENT! It makes your final adjustment permanent, because you have tightened the saddle before the beat is set.

Price $3.95 Each

AT LEADING MATERIAL HOUSES

*Trade Mark Registered, U. S. Patent Office

HOROLOVAR* 400-DAY CLOCK SUSPENSION SPRING UNITS — COMPLETE

These Suspension Units are equipped with a Horolovar Temperature Compensating Suspension Spring, and are assembled in a universal jig. The position of the blocks and fork, and the *strength*† of the spring, are guaranteed to be accurate in every respect for the clock and model specified. Repairmen whose time is at a premium will find these complete Horolovar Suspension Units a great convenience. No complete Suspension Units are available for clocks made prior to 1949.

†The width and thickness of the Horolovar Suspension Spring may not be the same as for the spring which it replaces, but its torsion characteristics are nevertheless correct.

Unit No.	Make and Model of Clock	Unit No.	Make and Model of Clock
1	Kundo Standard 49	23B	Reiner Standard 56
3A	Kundo Standard 53	25A	Hermle Standard 53
3B	Kundo Standard 54	25B	Hermle Miniature 54
3C	Kundo Standard 55	26	Wurthner Standard
5A	Kundo Junior 53	27A	Herr Standard 53
5B	Kundo Junior 54	27B	Herr Standard 55
5E	Kundo Junior 56	27C	Neueck Standard 57
5F	Kundo Midget 58	28A	Herr Miniature 53
6789	Schatz Standard 49	28B	Herr Miniature 54
10A	Schatz Miniature 53	28C	Herr Miniature 56
10B	Schatz 1000-Day 54	29A	Henn Miniature 52
10C	Schatz Midget 57	29B	Henn Miniature 53
11A	Kern Standard 50	31	Henn Standard 52
11B	Kern Standard 54	32	Henn Standard 54
12C	Kern Miniature 57	33	Jauch & Haller 54
12D	Kern Miniature 58	34	Kaiser Standard 54
12E	Kern Midget 58	35	Link Miniature 56
12F	Kern Miniature 61	36B	Petersen Standard 55
13B	Koma Standard 52	38	Koma Midget 57
13C	Koma Standard 56	40B	Crescent Standard 55 (Japan)
14A	Koma Miniature 54	41B	Master Standard 55 (Japan)
14B	Koma Miniature 65	42	Haller Standard 70
16	Link Standard 52	43	Haller Miniature 70
18C	Petersen Standard 54	44	Haller Midget 70
20A	Herr Standard 54	45	Master Standard 70 (Japan)
20B	Herr Standard 54	46	New Master 70 (Japan)
23A	Reiner Standard 53	47	Hermle Miniature 71

See Section 5 of this Guide for illustrations and descriptions of these Complete Suspension Units.

Price $2.35 Each

AT LEADING MATERIAL HOUSES

HOROLOVAR* 400-DAY CLOCK MAINSPRING WINDER

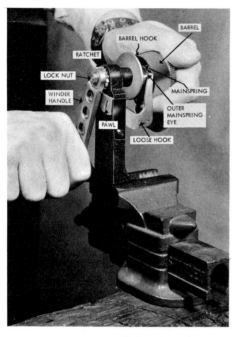

Clockmakers who insert mainsprings into 400-Day Clock barrels by hand not only distort the coils, with resulting loss of power, but also risk bruised or cut hands.

- For standard, miniature and midget clocks
- A safety ratchet holds wound spring firmly while barrel is being seated.
- Outer spring eye automatically attaches itself to the barrel hook.
- Winder arbor releases from inner spring eye without bending the coil.
- Will not distort the coil.
- Can be used for left or right hand winding springs.
- Holds firmly in vise.
- Built to last for generations!
- Satisfaction guaranteed or full refund will be made to buyer if returned within 10 days.

Price $22.50 Complete With 4 Interchangeable Arbors

HOROLOVAR* LONG ROUND TAPERED PINS — BRASS AND STEEL

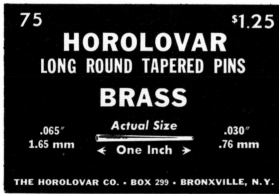

75   **$1.25**

HOROLOVAR
LONG ROUND TAPERED PINS
BRASS

.065″ *Actual Size* .030″
1.65 mm ◄ One Inch ► .76 mm

THE HOROLOVAR CO. · BOX 299 · BRONXVILLE, N.Y.

Packaged in patented snap-fastener envelope.

Save Time

No need to hunt for—or waste time filing—a steel or brass pin to fit. These long, round, tapered pins come in five sizes, fit practically any size hole in any clock: hand holding, dial lug, pillar, intermediate wheel post, suspension blocks, etc.

Look Better

New pins look neater, hold better. Bent or chewed pins make your best work seem sloppy.

Economical, too

The pins are all long, can often be cut in two pieces, each piece being used separately.

ENVELOPE COLOR	METAL	QUANTITY	LENGTH	SMALL DIAMETER	LARGE DIAMETER	ACTUAL SIZE
GREEN	STEEL			.012″ (.30 mm)	.050″ (1.27 mm)	
RED	BRASS			.025″ (.64 mm)	.065″ (1.65 mm)	
BLACK	STEEL	75	1.00″ (25.4 mm)			
BLUE	STEEL			.045″ (1.44 mm)	.075″ (1.91 mm)	
BROWN	BRASS	40	1.25″ (31.8 mm)	.070″ (1.78 mm)	.100″ (2.54 mm)	
GREY	BRASS	34		.095″ (2.41 mm)	.125″ (3.18 mm)	

Price $1.25 Each

AT LEADING MATERIAL HOUSES

*Trade Mark Registered, U. S. Patent Office

HOROLOVAR* 400-DAY CLOCK ADJUSTABLE PALLET SETTERS

FOR STANDARD CLOCKS

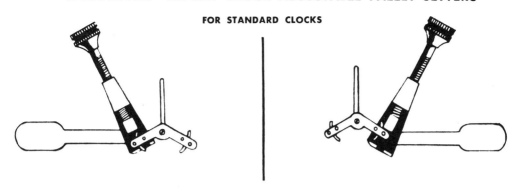

FOR MINIATURE CLOCKS

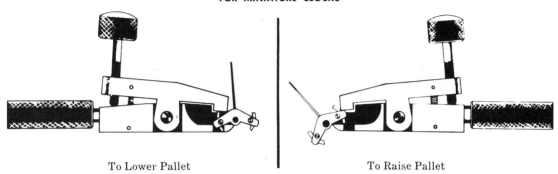

To Lower Pallet   To Raise Pallet

The tool offers you these advantages.

- Will raise or lower either right or left pallet with equal ease
- Will allow "micrometer" adjustments to be made
- Makes it unnecessary to loosen the holding screws before moving the pallet
- Cannot injure the pallets, because it is made of a soft alloy.

Price $9.95 Each

HOROLOVAR* MAINSPRING LET-DOWN KEYS

Prevent bruised knuckles and damaged wheel teeth! Use Horolovar's two let-down keys, especially designed to fit all 400-Day Clocks — Standard, Miniature and Midget models. The same keys will also fit most American and French mantel clocks. These keys are a must for all clock repairmen.

No. 610   Sizes 6   and 10   For Standard and Miniature Models
No. 2535   Sizes 2½ and 3½   For Midget models

Price $2.00 Each

AT LEADING MATERIAL HOUSES

*Trade Mark Registered, U. S. Patent Office

HOROLUBE 9·C*
A High Quality Lubricant for Clocks

NOW! For the *first* time . . .
a high-quality, low-cost lubricant,
especially designed for Clocks.

HOROLUBE 9·C is a balanced, general purpose lubricant composed of nine, non-evaporating ingredients, and having excellent fundamental lubricating characteristics. It is completely stabilized against corrosion and oxidation. Independent tests† of 16 domestic and imported watch and clock lubricants, conducted by a recognized authority, proved that HOROLUBE 9·C's resistance to spreading is greater than that of 15 of these lubricants, and fully equal to the 16th!

HOROLUBE 9·C is highly recommended for lubricating mechanical clocks of all types: mantel, wall, ship's, grandfather, carriage, regulator, traveling, torsion pendulum, etc., including those with jewelled escapements. Its stability, viscosity, low friction and great strength also qualify it highly as a mainspring lubricant.

HOROLUBE 9·C is superior in every way! It is virtually permanent. It will not evaporate, decompose, oxidize, corrode, or turn rancid. It is non-toxic and will not irritate. Its viscosity, having minimum variation at ordinary temperature ranges, is **perfect** for clocks.

HOROLUBE 9·C is economical! It costs less per ounce than any other quality lubricant. And you get more for your money. One bottle lubricates over 75 average size mantel clocks.

Preserve customer confidence and increase your reputation for long lasting repairs. Use only the **best** clock lubricant. Use HOROLUBE 9·C.

Price $1.50 Per 1 oz. Bottle   †Details on request

AT LEADING MATERIAL HOUSES

*Trade Mark Registered, U. S. Patent Office

168

SECTION 7 . . . . SPARE PARTS AND REPAIRS

Spare Parts

The Horolovar Company is the largest supplier of 400-Day Clock parts in the world. We not only stock parts for clocks which are in current German production, but we also have a large stock of parts for clocks out of production. Many of the latter have been obtained by cannibalizing old movements. Certain parts which are no longer available, but for which there is still a demand, we have made to order in quantity.

In 1953, peak year for 400-Day Clock manufacture, there were 13 German clock factories each making a variety of models. Most of these clocks reached the U. S., either through importation or as gifts purchased at Post Exchanges throughout the world. In 1965, only 5 manufacturers were still in 400-Day Clock production and most of these on a very limited scale. With each passing year, therefore, the maintenance of a spare parts inventory is an increasing problem, yet we are able to fulfill the vast majority of requirements.

How to Order

Order parts through your local watch material dealer or direct from The Horolovar Company. Identify the clock by the back plate number in this Repair Guide and describe, carefully, the part(s) needed. Using this system, it will not be necessary to submit a sample.
Samples *are* usually needed for clocks of pre-World War I manufacture whose movement back plates are marked only with a serial number or are not marked with the name of a manufacturer or importer.

Repairs

The Horolovar Company discontinued repair service in December, 1964. For several years prior to that date, we had solicited only the repair of "problem" clocks from the trade. Since the answer to each problem was usually to be found somewhere in the pages of this Guide, or could easily have been located by checking through the answer to Question 21 on page 35, it was felt that this service was not being used for the purpose intended.

If you are faced with a specific repair problem which you feel is not covered somewhere in this Guide, or if you have other questions about the clock, we will gladly try to help. Write: Question Department, The Horolovar Company, Box 400, Bronxville, New York 10708. If the question is about repair, give as many details about the symptoms, and the steps you have taken, as you possibly can. And ... *be sure to enclose a self-addressed, return envelope.*

Wanted - Old Movements and Pendulums

We are interested in purchasing movements and pendulums only, from certain out-of-production clocks, whether they are in working order or not. If you have any for sale, please do not send them. Instead, write us, giving the back plate numbers of the movements, as shown in Section 4, and state the approximate condition of both movement and pendulum. Address your letter to: Purchasing Department, The Horolovar Company, Box 400, Bronxville, New York 10708. We will tell you how much the parts are worth to us.

SECTION 8 . . . SOME OF THE OLD CLOCKS IN THE
HOROLOVAR 400-DAY CLOCK COLLECTION

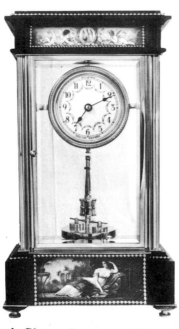

French Glass, Brass and Wood Case
with Paintings on Enamel   Trade Mark:
"Anniversary Clock"   17" High
Horolovar Plate No. 1007

Decorative Disc Pendulum
Glass and Wood Case   14" High
Horolovar Plate No. 1437

"Temperature Compensating" Pendulum
Inverted Balls   11" High
Horolovar Plate No. 1267

Calendar Clock   11" High
Days of Week and Month Dials
Horolovar Plate No. 1667

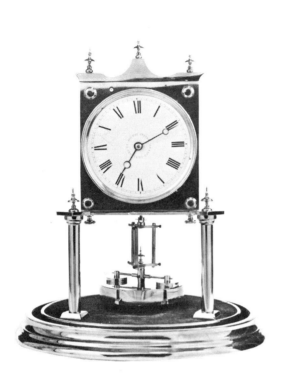

Hour and Half Hour Bell Strike
"De Gruyter's Patent"
Oval Glass Dome   14" High
Horolovar Plate No. 1473

Torsion Pendulum Clock
14 Day Movement   22" High

400-Day Clock Set
3-Ball Pendulum   16" High
Horolovar Plate No. 1179

Smallest "400-Day" Clock
Marble Base   6" High
Made By Kienzle
Horolovar Plate No. 1175

Hour and Half Hour Bell Strike
"Jahresuhr Sylvester"
Duplex Escapement
Oval Glass Dome   18" High
Horolovar Plate No. 1307

"Temperature Compensating" Pendulum
Chronometer Type   13" High
Glass and Brass Case
Horolovar Plate No. 1415

Skeleton Clock With
Skeleton Disc Pendulum
Oval Glass Dome   13" High
Horolovar Plate No. 1033

Front Wind Movement
Cylindrical Pendulum   32" High
Horolovar Plate No. 1623

"Governor" Type Pendulum
11" High
Horolovar Plate No. 1171

"Temperature Compensating" Pendulum
Twin Loop Type   11" High
Horolovar Plate No. 1043

Movement Has Four Supporting
Columns   11" High
Horolovar Plate No. 1047

Miniature Clock   8" High
Glass and Brass Case
Imported By LeRoy, Paris
Horolovar Plate No. 1631

Standard Clock   11" High
Glass and Brass Case
Imported By Tiffany & Co.
Horolovar Plate No. 1617

Rococo Frame   12" High
Horolovar Plate No. 1163

Overhead Suspension
Made By Gustav Becker   11" High
Horolovar Plate No. 1199

French Case
Unusual Pendulum Design
12" High
Horolovar Plate No. 1043

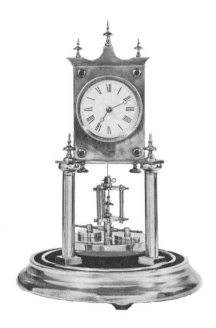

An Early Model   Has
First Type of Pendulum
Superstructure   11" High
Horolovar Plate No. 1603

Ball-type Disc Pendulum
11" High
Horolovar Plate No. 1419

Has Removable Crown Covering Top
of Glass Dome   15" High
Horolovar Plate No. 1047

Combination Torsion AND Helical
Spring Clock   24" High
14 Day Movement
Full Hour and Half Hour Strike

"Temperature Compensating" Pendulum
Chronometer Type   13" High
Takes 7" x 12" Glass Dome
Horolovar Plate No. 1415

"Temperature Compensating" Pendulum
Moving Lever Type   11" High
Horolovar Plate No. 1055

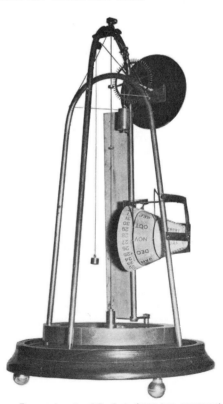

Inventor's Model (REAR VIEW)
A One-wheel Torsion Pendulum
Clock With a Tiny "Cylinder"
Type Anchor   17" High